TIMELESS LAND

Evening at Ben Ohau 1994 Oil on Canvas 715 x 1120mm Collection: Locations Realty Ltd, Queenstown

TIMELESS LAND

Painter
GRAHAME SYDNEY

Poet
BRIAN TURNER

Writer
OWEN MARSHALL

with an Introduction by **SAM NEILL**

Longacre Press

ACKNOWLEDGEMENTS

Longacre Press and **Grahame Sydney** sincerely thank the owners of the paintings for their co-operation and support.

We also thank the photographers who photographed the original works, many of which are housed in private collections all over New Zealand. Their combined attention to detail and perseverence is appreciated, and is displayed in the superb reproductions shown here: Ross Coombes, Dunedin; Becky Nunes, Auckland; Lloyd Park, Christchurch; John Crawford, New Plymouth.

Photographs on pages 158 and 159 are by Reg Graham.

Many of the stories and poems in this book have appeared in previous publications:

Owen Marshall

'There is a Place', excerpts from *A Many Coated Man* (Longacre, 1995); 'Body and Soul', 'Cabernet Sauvignon with my Brother', 'Descent from the Flugelhorn' and 'Requiem in a Town House' from *The Divided World* (McIndoe, 1989); 'Dungarvie Festival' from *Tomorrow We Save the Orphans* (McIndoe, 1992); 'Sully's Country' from *The Day Hemingway Died and other stories* (McIndoe, 1984).

Brian Turner

'Afternoon', 'Madness and the Mountain', 'Watch for the Ice' and 'The Stopover' in *Ladders of Rain* (McIndoe, 1978); 'Ancestors' and 'Silver Birches' in *Ancestors* (McIndoe, 1981); 'Elegy in the Clutha Valley' and 'Grass' in *Listening to the River* (McIndoe, 1983); 'On the Edge of a Meadow' and 'Lawrence Cemetery' in *Bones* (McIndoe, 1985); 'Abandoned Homestead', 'Crossing the Canterbury Plains', 'Flight', 'Naming the Lost', 'Place', 'Salvation's Army', 'Tangata Whenua', 'Under the Hawkduns', and 'Walking In' in *All that Blue Can Be* (McIndoe, 1989); 'Clouds', 'Landscapes of Central Otago', and 'Van Morrison in Central Otago' in *Beyond* (McIndoe, 1992).

The poems 'A Procession of Clouds', 'Central Otago', 'Earthday', 'Kyeburn', 'Spaces' and 'Towards the Maniototo' have not been published before. These are selected from a group of new poems written during the period I was in receipt of a Scholarship in Letters awarded by the then Arts Council of New Zealand (Toi Aotearoa). The Council's support is gratefully acknowledged.

First published with the assistance of Creative New Zealand, Arts Council of New Zealand *Toi Aotearoa*.

ISBN 1 877135 71 2

First published in 1995 in a limited edition of 300 copies individually numbered and signed by the contributing three artists.

Standard edition published in 1995
Standard edition reprinted in 1996
Standard edition reprinted in 2002, 2004

Published by Longacre Press Ltd.,
30 Moray Place, Dunedin, New Zealand

Technical Details
Book cover design by Christine Buess.
Book design by Jenny Cooper.
Printed by Everbest Printing Company Ltd, China.
Electronic pre-press by Hughes Lithographics, Dunedin.

CONTENTS

INTRODUCTION BY SAM NEILL

My Dad. My Dad took us for holidays in Central. He was a delightful man in many ways, but far from practical. We had an old Bedford van into which children and camping gear would be crammed, with more gear piled on top, badly secured by an old clothesline. The journey was always edged with a little tension as to what would fly off next. We also had a succession of dreadful boats towed on old rusty trailers. Dad couldn't resist them, and was always being cheated by Blokes who looked like they knew What Was What.

Dad's holiday gear was like him, ex-army: khaki shirts where you could see the missing crowns on the epaulettes, and excruciatingly baggy shorts. Only on holiday did you see Dad's ghastly knobbly knees, identical to my own as it happens.

The journey was like life, never easy. Apart from the fear of being forever separated from some critical piece of equipment, like the boat, there was the Fear of Car Sickness. My sister and I were great pukers. And the Great Fear of the Shingle Road. Most roads were unsealed then and our van was seemingly always full of choking, blinding dust, the same colour as Dad's shorts.

The road started getting interesting just before Roxburgh. Before that it was all gorse, winding roads and nausea. Here we'd stop to buy cherries and apricots, each one an intimation of the Paradise to Come. Further on before Alexandra, Dad always said it was just like Palestine where he'd served before the War, in the same shorts. If I squinted my eyes, I could almost see Christ out there in the Otago wilderness.

It was around here you'd notice the first motor camp. Now if there was one thing in the world that Dad despised, it was a Motor Camp. The idea of driving 200 miles to live cheek-by-jowl with the Common Man filled him with an irrational horror. This phobia we encouraged; the further from everyone else we were, the less likely the Common Man was to witness Dad's knobbly knees and his cursing incompetence when it came to erecting our clumsy ex-army equipment. Civilians, not for the use of.

No, the communal joy of the Motor Camp was not for us. Nor the sybaritic comfort of the Wanaka bach. We were made of sterner stuff. On we'd grind into sandfly territory, and as the light was leaving the tops, our hearts were full of conflicting emotions. Dad, dear old reserved Dad, would shout with startling joy as rounding a corner we'd first see The River or The Lake. But there was also the Terrible Fear of not finding the right camping site before nightfall. Dad could really pick them, especially after dark. More than once we were flooded out in the night, and another time we were memorably blown right off the hill by a nor'wester.

Eventually though we'd end up somewhere brilliant, and aside from the occasional spot of rain which always made Dad unutterably miserable, these were easily the best days of our young lives. Here I learnt the incomparable pleasure of fishing. One of the dreadful boats was just fast enough to waterski behind if the lake was mirror calm, which it often was. I learnt how to stay downwind of the aromatic manuka-fuelled thermette to avoid the sandfly. But more than all of this, I learnt directly from my Dad an intense love for this particular part of the world, this very particular landscape. And still today, when I am away from it, I am filled with a longing to be back there. And I am always aware of the sad irony of the impossibility of living where you feel most at home.

Dad must have learnt this from *his* father; I have photos of my grandfather, Sid, with beautiful fat brown trout, and wearing even baggier shorts than Dad. And there they are, the same hilariously knobbly knees. Sid once survived a week cut off by a flooded Makarora by shooting a hapless heifer. One of Sid's uncles incidentally was killed in a coaching accident near Roxburgh. What happened? Did he fall off, nauseated after the trip from Lawrence? Was the McRae's

Flat Pub too much for him? Was he crushed under an avalanche of badly secured luggage?

Ah, Central, the site of family triumph and disaster. Central. The deep heart of the South Island of New Zealand. Central. The subject of this book. Grahame Sydney, Owen Marshall and Brian Turner sing together about Central, together they bring clarity and light to the particular, they celebrate the unique. I think they, like me, are saying "Where else would you want to be from?"

With growing familiarity, my favourite part of Central has become perhaps the least obvious; the Maniototo. Quintessential Otago. I owe this understanding in part to my friend Grahame Sydney, and the shock of recognition his paintings bring. Recognition not only of the physicality of the place, its silent beauty. But also recognition of how you *feel* in that place, recognition of oneself. The exhilaration of solitude that is inseparable from the terror of loneliness.

The best approach to the Maniototo is the road from Outram. I prefer it to the all too easy back road from Alexandra or the deviously covert Pig Root. No, this way is heroic. From Outram you climb the hills under the Taieri Pet, such a fond name for a cloud that looks like the aftermath of an apocalypse. When you reach the top, if you can stand at all in the inevitable gale, you have the view of the Gods. A blasted rocky foreground, the whalesback of the Rock and Pillar Range glowering to the left, and forever in the distance the mythical Hawkduns. Spread below you is Strath Taieri, a savagely blended Maori and Scots title for the wildest of flats. From there a low pass to the Maniototo, a vast dry valley surrounded by bare hills.

Here the climate is, at best, volatile. Stay for only an hour and, like Crowded House, you will know four seasons in one day. Once last year I drove in under a black sky. Overnight, snow had fallen and the place was monochromatically splendid. I stopped in Ranfurly, had a cup of tea and a perfect whitebait fritter, and the sun came out.

By the time I was off again, the snow had all but gone and a skylark was singing.

That sound. When you look at Grahame's paintings, it's good to provide yourself with your own soundtrack. Possibly a skylark, at the least some wind. I often favour the falcon. *Karearea* the Maori call them, and that is the sound that they make. It is the loneliest sound in the world.

Speaking of sound, I would also recommend reading Brian Turner's astringent austere poetry aloud, in a quiet place. Behind the woolshed perhaps. And Owen Marshall's wry astute stories are best read alone. In silence. When I look at the work of all three, I always like to ask "What happens next?" Will Ros walk away, or will she turn and say something? What?

What happens next for *me* is that I will return once more. It has become a seasonal migratory thing. And every time I do, I have the strongest sense of my Dad in the landscape, just as he must have missed his Dad in the same place. I hope that after I'm gone, my children will sense me there too, knobbly-kneed in my own khaki shorts, squinting into the wind. For how can you separate the man from the land?

SAM NEILL
Lucca, Tuscany
Italy
8 October 1995

PLACE

Once in a while
you may come across a place
where everything
seems as close to perfection
as you will ever need.
And striving to be faultless
the air on its knees
holds the trees apart,
yet nothing is categorically
thus, or that, and before the dusk
mellows and fails
the light is like honey
on the stems of tussock grass,
and the shadows
are mauve birthmarks
spreading
from the hills.

ABANDONED HOMESTEAD

A family lived here   in this homestead
on a terrace   above a wide valley
with a river running down   to a glacial lake

In the distance are mountains   blue and black
and   closer   the river winding
thin and waxy like floss

Dust   droppings   cobwebs   straw
the house is full of signs of uninvited guests
and on a shelf beside the range
I find a piece of wood
inscribed with the words   Agnes Brown toiled here

To my knowledge   there is no other record
of what she thought or said   so we're not
going to know   what she did
when the man she lived with   was riding
the farthest boundaries of the run

And we can only imagine   what she said
to her children   when they left home
headed for the big smoke   one supposes
they drove off   harness jangling   dust
puffing from hoofs and wheels   the cart
rocking and bouncing along the track   but
how long she stood there   after the cart
had gone   we cannot say

The summer evenings are long here
and we assume she sat   on the verandah
knitting or reading   watching the ridges
for the shape of a man on a horse
silhouetted against the flare
from the setting sun

More than a lifetime has passed   and the wood
where I sit   on that same verandah
is rotted now   and the evening light's
like panic   on the cracked windows
behind me   and in the west
the sky is tangerine   and the mountains turning black

LANDSCAPES OF CENTRAL OTAGO

(after Sydney)

So familiar, enduring, and vast
those never-ending spaces, landscapes
leaning, expanding, receding, stricken
like the feelings some take for love.

Skies that stretch and strain the land's colours,
their light colouring light; and high
taut blues which seep into yellow
and deepen over the duns, the browns
of your lazy Central hills.

All's time-worn, defiant;
the skies lock in, and out, a longing
for the best
of what's not quite bygone. Here
past, present, and future
are stilled in paintings that,
as Lowell wrote,
'Pray for the grace of accuracy
Vermeer gave to the sun's illumination
stealing like the tide across a map
to his girl solid with yearning.'

Something inherent, pervasive as memory
is slowed beyond the frames,
behind hills and homes that, striving
for permanence, are solid only
with a yearning for what
is strange, alien, bygone.

Railway Red
1975
Egg Tempera on Gesso
597 x 832mm
Collection: Hocken Library, Dunedin

Wedderburn
1975
Egg Tempera on Gesso
610 x 725mm
Collection: H. Friedlander, Auckland

EARTHDAY

April   and it's that time again
the sun's unindulgent
    meaner   is low enough
to scrutinise our faces all day
    autumn's interlocutor

And something   probably air
    is moving the tussock
over there   by the river
    and something else
plucks the heartstrings   just a little
    because there's space
to do nothing   about nothing
    and nothing nags
quite as much   as it did

But what is *It* ?   well
    the sun's it   the breeze
is it   the river's tootling
    between swishy banks
is it   and so's St Bathans
    and the Dunstans   and the
Old Man Range growing older
    it's the world's ill   it's oneself
within oneself   everywhere you are
    everywhere you go

Slow Sign
1975
Egg Tempera on Gesso
610 x 560mm
Collection: R. A. & E. G. Brebner, Auckland

July on the Maniototo
1975
Egg Tempera on Gesso
750 x 585mm
Private Collection

On the Dogtrials
1976
Egg Tempera on Gesso
268 x 648mm
Private Collection

McCloskey, Gimmerburn
1975
Egg Tempera on Gesso
457 x 915mm
Collection: David & Dian Ross

THERE IS A PLACE ...

There is a place in the hills where no one wins farmer of the year; high up where the road is still unsealed and has bulges on its length occasionally so that if you're unlucky enough to meet something coming the other way, it can be decided by eye contact and gross tonnage who will back down — and then back up. Much of the land has beaten its proprietors, and so is given over to pine forest, and if the stands are immature the pruned branches are rust filagree beneath the velvet green of the firs. The farm houses are weatherboard and the sheds mainly shot. The dogs are kennelled in a gully head where the mutton bones go to die, and the white leghorns flap up into nooks of the equipment shed to roost, where they mute on the harnesses and the post-hole digger which have no other use. There are boxes and bags of apparently unused seed, but the birds and the mice have long since been in and all can be winnowed away. There's a tractor seat cover made from possum pelts and stirrup pumps that have never worked and refuse to start doing so now. In the shearing shed the wood is richly stained with fleece oil and dags and a little blood and sweat. A track winds over the gorse-covered top of the gully to the manuka country beyond and slopes of pigfern rooted over by the namesake, and screes of serpentine rock which make a cheap fence because the sheep will hardly cross, and a high pond or two which you'd never know were there, but the stock tracks wind their way to them and the mallards which can be covered with a couple of guns. Pretty much dry country most of the time, and the hack still better than the farm bike, but there are days when the cloud comes in, the gorse and briar glisten almost as much as the serpentine, the manuka stems gradually darken as the rain seeps through, the pigfern is bowed down by the weight of the drops it bears.

There are ridges and faces and gullies and spurs that don't appear on maps. They're given names by the family who have to climb them and when the people go they take away the names. There's a place where beech were sledded down to make the first houses and there's a place in the creek, a small falls, where the biggest boar was stuck, whose tusks hang over the shearing shed and glint in the evening sun. No matter who does the muster, no matter how keen the dogs, there are a few old woollies on every place that never come down to the yards. But you know all that.

SULLY'S COUNTRY

The basin country was yellow-ginger and rounded in the sun; sprawled in the sun, and there was a shimmer of heat from the road and the bare river line like a scar. Sully looked as if he'd died at the wheel. Not much steering movement was needed on the straight. His eyes were partly closed because of the glare, and his mouth was partly open. The stub of a rolled cigarette was stuck to his lower lip. Moisture from his mouth had brought the stain of the tobacco through the paper. Sully's hands were together at the top of the wheel, not gripping it but hanging over it, so that his fingers were loose on the other side and trembled with the vibration of the wheel. 'It's not far to the turn-off now,' said Sully, as if to prove he was alive. He eased the stub from his lip in case it had stuck to the skin. It was out, but he squeezed it deliberately before flicking it from the utility.

At the turn-off there was a wooden box on a concrete pedestal. It had tin on top like a dog kennel, but it was bigger and had a door with a simple catch; a piece of wood with a nail in the centre. There was no name on it, and although we could see all round for several miles there was no sign of the homestead. Sully swung round the corner and stopped, unconcerned that the utility blocked the road. 'I wouldn't think Clem will be long,' he said. He got out and stood for a moment listening for an engine; watching for any dust. The only noise was the pinging of the truck metal. I walked over to the box, just to move about a bit again. There was nothing in it except a ten pound tin of honey, and some tailing bands scattered on the floor. 'If he can't make it we'll leave the drench and that in there,' said Sully.

There was no shade anywhere outside the car, and we were forced back to it again, and sat askew on the seat with the doors open to invite movement of the air. 'I was at the sale-yards at five thirty this morning,' said Sully. It was his explanation for leaning back and closing his eyes. His mouth sagged open as the muscles of his face

relaxed. The lines from his eyes radiated like the markings of a scallop shell, and as he slept they showed paler against his brown face. His hands were cupped, and the left one flipped on the seat suddenly in response to a random nerve; like the death of a fish in the bottom of a dinghy. It woke him up for a few seconds. 'Yes, it's sleepy weather all right,' he said. 'You don't mind.' He slept again, and the character that his face had in wakefulness was replaced by a mere assortment of features; things incidental to the inner Sully.

I lay back and tried to rest too. I could tell by the band of my watch that my hands were swollen, and a pulse beat at the back of my eyes so that the image of the hills was doubly blurred. I imagined a bottle of German Riesling, so cold that condensation would cloud the outside of the glass, and I thought how I might roll the bottle on my forehead before I drank. There were no sheep visible on the tussock, and no birds in all of the sky. So still and quiet I could hear a faint buzz, like that from high-tension wires, but there were no wires and the humming must have been the heat in the air, or the blood in my ears. There was not even a fly to enjoy our sweat.

When we did hear a vehicle, Sully woke in instant possession of himself. He was more accustomed to the heat. 'This will be him,' he said. We caught glimpses of a Landrover on the terraces across the riverbed, and patches of dust hung in the air like signals. Sully passed the time by making himself a cigarette, and picking stones from the rubber tread of his boots. The Landrover reached the straight on our side, and bore down on us. It stopped in front, in the middle of the road like us. 'He's got his son Stuart with him,' said Sully, as we got out.

'Hello Sully,' said Clem.

'This heat again,' said Sully. 'It's drying everything up.'

'It's bloody dry at the moment,' said Clem.

'Clem, this is Brian Marfell, the area accountant. I'm taking him around to show him where the work is really done in the firm.'

'This is the sharp end all right,' said Clem. He shook my hand. 'Brian Marfell,' he said firmly, as a man does who hears few new names, and would remember it. 'The streak here is my son Stuart,' he said. Stuart grinned, and crunched his big boots in the gravel. He must have been about six four. He wore an orange towelling hat which hung on a face so thin that it was always in profile. All his height was in his legs. Gangling, ostrich legs of long muscles, and bleached hairs against the brown skin. He had two layers of socks on, and they were folded down over the tops of his boots, so accentuating the length of his legs. Clem was dark and square. Beside him Stuart was all ostrich legs and profile.

'When will you do your main shear?' said Sully.

'We start mustering tomorrow,' said Clem. 'That's why I was glad you could bring this stuff up today.'

'Well, we were coming up as far as Latrobes anyway.' We began taking Clem's stuff from the truck to the Landrover, and Sully and he continued to talk business. It seemed a tribute to human planning that in all those empty miles we could coincide and concentrate two vehicles and four people. Our voices in the hot air bled away without any barriers.

'There's some honey in the box,' I said. Clem added it to his load. Sully dropped a bag of eartags. The bag burst, and the eartags were spilled like amazing green beans in the dust and gravel.

'I want a cut on those,' said Clem. 'They're delivered dirty.'

'You'll be lucky. See the accountant,' said Sully.

'You know how they choose accountants,' I said.

'The tightest arses in the firm,' said Sully. Stuart laughed. He was trying to find hinges in his stilt legs, so that he could get down to pick up some of the tags.

'Come back to the homestead,' Clem said. 'We'll have a beer or

something.' Sully looked at me. He didn't think we could spare the time, but he didn't like to say, because I was the guest on the trip. I said it was kind, but that we'd best keep moving. 'I'll tell you what then,' said Clem. 'Call in at the old Dun Lilluch place. There's beer there, although it won't be cold because there's no power. Snaffle a few bottles for yourself, and if Morris is there, remind him we begin mustering tomorrow.'

Stuart squeezed back into the Landrover, and his knees were almost level with his ears as he used clutch and accelerator. He grinned as he made a final sweep to turn, and then we could see only the vehicle's back. 'The muster tomorrow is just a dawdle for that lad,' said Sully. 'He'll walk to hell and back in a day.' We watched the Landrover diminish down the straight, and then disappear on to the first river terrace. The noise altered as soon as it wasn't in direct line. 'On our way I suppose,' said Sully. 'At least we can generate a bit of a draught on the move. Clem's a good client with us, and a big one.'

Sully and I talked idly for a bit after we got started again. He told me that Morris was one of the station shepherds, and he described Clem's pasture management plans, but the heat beat us again, and by the time the old Dun Lilluch house came into view I was lolling on the headrest. Sully said the house was only used when one of the shepherds, or the fencers, had work to do in that part of the run. The house had hay in all the rooms except kitchen, bathroom and sitting room. The front door was boarded up, but the windows on that side of the house had no glass, and the sills were worn with the passage of hay bales in and out.

The back door wasn't locked, and Sully found a carton of beer under the kitchen bench. Morris had been sleeping in the corner of the sitting room. A palliasse and blankets were there, and a transistor on the bare timber of the floor. We took our beer on to the shady side of the house, and sat on the warm ground. Even there our breathing was quick and shallow. We were closer to the river than before. There were runs of fine silt amongst the stones, and smears of mud in hollows dried to the colour of dust. But there was no visible water. The tussock hills across the riverbed baked yellow-ginger in the sun, and there was nothing that was green. 'In the winter,' said Sully, 'there can be several feet of snow here for weeks on end.' Yet it was difficult to believe the sun would ever lose its sovereignty over the place. The beer was warm, almost soapy, in my mouth.

'You must know the place almost as well as the locals,' I said.

'This has been part of my area for twenty-three years. And all the years I've been on the road have been with the same firm. It doesn't change much, this sort of country. What we see now is what it's always been, I suppose.' Sully's affection wasn't sentimental. 'It's not easy country to farm at all,' he said.

Sully got an auctioneer's card from the utility, and wrote on it, thanks for the beer — Clem says remember the muster — Sully. He left the card by Morris's transistor, and closed the back door behind us, pulling hard on the dented brass knob. I had a leak by the truck. The ground was so hard it didn't soak in, but gathered a film of dust and ran like mercury over the ground.

Had we waited any longer before leaving, Morris would have met us at the house. As it was we saw the motorbike when we had gone barely a mile, and Sully stopped again. Morris had no helmet. He wore shorts, singlet and boots. He had a soft hat stuffed into his pocket. The farm bike had a carrier tray, and from it a dog jumped down and sniffed the tyres of the truck. Morris sat on his bike in the sun, and folded his arms to talk to us. I had a conviction that I'd seen him before, and Sully glanced at me with an odd smile. Then it came to me. He was the same as Stuart. Morris was older, early fifties maybe, but the same axe face always in profile, and the same legs too long for his body. Daddy-long-legs, though Morris's had lost some of

their earlier tautness and were wrinkled and pouchy at the knees. Morris was inviting us back for more beer, but we thought not. We talked some more, until Sully had rolled himself another smoke, and then we parted. Morris reared up and settled one great boot on the slender kick-start. The dog jumped up at the sound of the engine, and for a while dust and the two-stroke smell hung in the still air.

Sully seemed to think it appropriate that we had met Morris. He whistled softly as he drove on, and his expression was nonchalant. 'All right,' I said, 'I'm going to say it. What's the set-up there? Morris and Stuart and Clem.'

'I've never asked,' said Sully. 'It's nothing to do with me.'

'Stuart must be Morris's boy.'

'Who's going to say it?' said Sully. 'Clem's got one son, he's happily married, he owns a lease on 20,000 acres. You name me anyone who gains by changing things.'

'But Morris, still working on the place?' I said.

'Things here are rarely what they seem. A dozen different stories could be the truth. Nothing is real once it has happened. I don't know.' Sully looked over his country; the terraces and ridges were marked more harshly as the sun was falling. There were subtle changes in the colours of the land, and heat was giving way to silence as the greater presence. 'They're not much on appearances, the people out here,' said Sully. 'They're interested in what works.'

Fog at Stan Cotter's
1975
Egg Tempera on Gesso
915 x 432mm
Private Collection

LAWRENCE CEMETERY

(for Ngaire)

An artist takes snaps of cemeteries
irresistibly, *click*, with light
angling in from the left, say,
or the right, shadows staining headstones
and neglected plots, rusty iron
fencing off the last small pieces of land
that are definitely not ours.
One walks with care on such impenitent ground.

The sun dazzles and sprags
like a splinter in the corner
of your eye. Late light genuflects
upon the nearby hills: distantly
mountains turn gun-metal blue.
It feels quite neighbourly, you say,
picking a path among the broken vases
and the perky faces of wild flowers.

ELEGY IN THE CLUTHA VALLEY

(In memory of Denis Glover)

Something we will never know
the reason for
or the answer to
woke me one January morning
and streamed through the half-open window
and made me feel it was timeless,

and I remembered a day
that will always be long ago
when I was older
and better able
to stride off over the rolling downs
in search of all the best reasons

in the beleaguered world
to do or not to do,
and to be in touch with oneself
wherever heart and mind
had come to agree
on where we should be going,

and let us think this
could be so. Then, the world's ill
flew from the shoulder
of the highest hill
around, and thereafter the will
took a bolder part in things

and my heart leapt
to the blind mountain
from which scree flaked
and water bled all day long
to the downy valley floor
where, in the evening

I took my rod and my heart
to the river's side
and cast and cast
while the water
ran purple and gold
in the quickening dusk,

and the sedges
fleeing the river
were like ash
at my face and throat
and all the world
seemed to be timeless.

Summer Piece
1976
Egg Tempera on Gesso
387 x 763mm
Collection: Mr & Mrs A. E. Taylor, Christchurch

SILVER BIRCHES

Autumn undresses us.
Such spare frames
have the silver birch,
such rueful responses
we share
over the lost chances
of previous seasons.

Chevrolet
1977
Egg Tempera on Gesso
300 x 570mm
Collection: Ashley Muir, Dunedin

Charlie's Bar
1977
Egg Tempera on Gesso
370mm x 560mm
Fletcher Challenge Art Collection

CABERNET SAUVIGNON WITH MY BROTHER

I walked the last three kilometres to my brother's place. I was lucky to have hitched as close as I did. Along the flat through Darfield and Kirwee early in the morning I'd done a good deal of walking, but then a tractor repair man took me to within three kilometres. He told me he'd been working on the hydraulics of a new Case harvester which cost eighty thousand dollars.

I love the accumulated heat of the Canterbury autumn. When you rest on the ground you can feel the sustained warmth coming up into your body, and there are pools of dust like talcum powder along the roads. It's not the mock tropicality of the far north, but the real New Zealand summer. It dries the flat of your tongue if you dare to breathe through your mouth. After spending the vacation working on the Coast, I was happy to be back in Canterbury.

My brother Raf lived on seventeen hectares of gravel close to West Melton. He had been a tutor in economics at Lincoln, but resigned on a matter of principle. He said it was a form of hypocrisy to pretend to any skill in financial affairs, when the best salary he could command was that of a tutor. Raf said that the most important things to achieve in life were privacy and revenue. At West Melton on seventeen hectares he had privacy, but the income was precarious. Raf's best crop was manoeuvres. He said he received a small but consistent return from manoeuvres. The army paid him for access to the river bed. Heavy manoeuvres was the better paying crop, he said, but harder on the ground.

As I walked up the natural terrace to Raf's place, the heat shimmer on the river bed was already beginning. The stones in Raf's paddocks didn't seem to have become any less numerous. I noticed that because last time I visited my brother, he told me that ploughing only brought them up, and that picking them off was uneconomic. Raf believed that if the ground was grazed naturally, and just a little super added from time to time, then worm action would increase the

height of the soil until the stones were eventually covered right over. He said he read a report of French research on it in Brittany. Raf had a knack of finding theoretical justification for his lifestyle.

He was working on his motorbike when I arrived. It was an old Norton 500 cc, an enormous single pot machine, and his only form of transport. With it he towed a trailer large enough for ten bales of hay. He left the front tube hanging from the tyre, and came down the track to meet me. 'Ah, Tony,' he said, and took me by the shoulder. 'I hoped to see you before the term began.' His blue eyes seemed bleached from the sun, and his hair and eyebrows were nearly white. 'I told myself you'd come,' he said. Although he was my brother, he was about fourteen years older than me; we were like uncle and nephew in some ways. I was aware of the emphasis and undisguised pleasure in his voice. 'I sold another dozen lambs last week.' To have revenue to share, as well as privacy, made him feel his hospitality was complete.

'I can't stay the night. Lectures start tomorrow. I should have been in today, really.'

'Well, we've the day together then,' said Raf, 'and you'll get out some time during the term.'

I went with Raf into his house, and he put into his pigmy fridge as many bottles of beer as it would hold. The kitchen floor had a slant, and when the fridge was operating the vibration caused it to creep from the wall, inch by inch. I could see it, as we sat at the table with our coffee, shuffling up to Raf's shoulder like a prototype robot. 'It takes about an hour to reach the table,' said Raf. He tolerated it because it never broke down; just had to be pushed back to the wall every hour. 'I have to switch it off when I go outside,' he said.

Raf felt no obligation to ask about our parents. Not that he disliked them; it was his way of showing that his friendship with me was apart from any other connection between us. He knew I'd tell him anything that he should know. 'You seem happy here still,' I said.

'Happiness is related to the level of expectation,' said Raf, and he pushed back the fridge. 'To be the mayor of Wellington, or the second richest farmer in Southland, is a gnawing futility if you can only be satisfied by being Prime Minister. Our education system should be directed to inculcating as low an expectation as possible in every child, and then most of them could grow up to be happy.' Raf's spur of the moment principle paid no heed to envy, but then he was working from the premise of his own nature. My brother was one of the minority who didn't compare themselves with others. He was self-sufficient in his ideas and ambitions. He enjoyed simple things; like being able to produce a meal for me from his property. We went outside, taking some beer with us, and I helped Raf to fix the front tube. As we did so, he laid out his plans for our lunch. 'If only we'd had rain,' he said, 'then there would have been mushrooms. I've been spreading the spores year by year. Now I get cartons full at times, and take them in to sell. Everything's right for them now, except the rain.'

'I'm not all that fussed on them anyway,' I said, just so that he wouldn't feel my expectation had been high.

'I've been saving some rabbits though. Down by the pines. And I've got plenty of eggs and vegetables. We could have chook, but fresh game is better.' Raf thought we should cull the rabbits before we had too much beer, and we went off over the stones and brown grass of his seventeen hectares towards the pines. 'You're doing accounting and economics, aren't you,' he said.

'Law. I'm doing law.'

'I found there wasn't much privacy in economics. I should say that law would be much the same; more revenue probably, but no privacy.' Raf stopped, and enjoyed the privacy of his land for a moment. The small terraces and scarps vibrated in the heat. The bird calls were outnumbered by the muted sound of firing from the West Melton butts. 'I've been thinking of going out of sheep into Angora goats,' said Raf. 'I read an article saying they're much more profitable per head; ideal for smaller properties. Three rabbits?' He tagged on about the rabbits after a pause, when we had started to walk towards the pines again. 'Is one and a half rabbits enough for you?'

'Fine.'

'I've been keeping an eye on these. There's nearly a dozen here. I've been looking forward to a special occasion so I could use some.' Raf walked in an arc behind the pines, so that we would come from the broken slope where there was gorse and briar. He shot two rabbits quickly with the twelve gauge, and then had me walk through the pines and flush another out to make the three.

Raf and I sat on the front step of his house, and he cleaned the rabbits as I peeled the potatoes. He went over the various ways in which the rabbits could be combined with the other food we had. We ate those rabbits several times over before we had lunch. They were good at last though, with potatoes, pumpkin, cheese sauce, boiled eggs and beer. Repletion made Raf even more relaxed and thoughtful. 'You get plenty of girls at the university I suppose,' he asked me. For the first time there was a hint of dissatisfaction in his voice. 'Girls don't seem much interested in privacy. I had a woman out here before Xmas. She did a lot of screen printing. She seemed to like it here for several weeks, but then she began to mope. She said she found the landscape oppressive. She wasn't a very tall girl, but big where it mattered, mind you.' My brother was at a loss to explain why anyone should prefer the city. 'I have to go into Christchurch now,' he said. There was a note of grievance. He saw it as a lack of consideration; the screen printing girl choosing to go back to town.

'Maybe it's the old house,' I said. 'Women have higher expectations there, I suppose.'

'I bought a new bed for us. A brass one, original. It cost me a fat lamb cheque. She hated anything artificial; plastic, vinyl, nylon, veneers, anything like that.' There certainly wasn't much of such material in Raf's house; almost everything looked pre-war. Even the walls were tongue and groove. 'She was a nice girl in many ways,' Raf said.

In mid-afternoon a visitor came. 'It's McLay,' Raf said. 'He's bought the big place up the road. I forgot all about him. He's come to look at my bore and pump.' McLay was a farmer of self-importance, one of these men who walk in a perfectly normal manner, but whose evident conceit makes them appear to swagger. He parked his European car at an angle which best displayed its lines, and his sense of complacency grew as he came closer to the house.

'Seen better days I'd say,' he said, and he tapped with his shoe at the decayed boards close to the ground along the front of the house. 'I like a place in permanent materials myself,' he said. 'Always have, always will.' Raf was never defensive about his property. He considered it too much of a blessing to need its weaknesses concealed.

'Most of the exterior is shot,' he said frankly. 'We had rabbit for lunch.' McLay was somewhat baffled by that, and suffered a subtle loss of initiative.

McLay would have taken his car to the pump, but Raf said it was easier if we sat in the trailer behind the Norton. McLay found it difficult to maintain his dignity there. He sat very upright, with one hand on the side to limit the bouncing, and with the other he tried to repel Raf's greasy tools, which clattered around us. Raf had one bore sunk into the gravel, and he ran off water to his troughs. When he reached the place he switched off the motor-bike, and sat there enjoying the sun. 'Never seems to run dry, this bore,' he said. 'It's with the river being so close I suppose.' McLay had scrambled from

the trailer, and was wiping his wrist on the grass to clean it, after warding off Raf's grease-gun. He felt a need to disassociate himself from Raf's scale of farming.

'I'll need to put in perhaps a dozen of these bores,' he told me. 'I've 350 hectares you see, and I hope to irrigate from them as well.'

'I only need to run it for an hour or so each day,' said Raf. He lifted the rusted kerosene tin which protected the motor.

'Mine will have to be electric, with remote switches. I won't be able to spend all day mucking about with petrol engines,' countered McLay. Raf wound up the starting cord, and pulled with no result. 'Gives a bit of trouble does it,' said McLay. Raf tried again and again. The only result was one cough, which flicked the starting cord up to give Raf a stinging blow across the face. McLay gave an understanding laugh. 'Pity it's not Briggs and Stratton. They're the only small motor, I always say. I think you've flooded it.' Raf seized the choke, fully extended it, and bent it across the motor. McLay was quiet. Two veins began to swell beneath the skin of my brother's forehead. They made an inverted Y the colour of a bruise. He tried twice more with the cord, attempts of elaborate calmness, then he went to the trailer and brought back the crow-bar. He systematically beat the four-stroke motor until the various attached parts had broken away. The crow-bar made a solid crump, crump sound of impact, and the pipe from the bore rattled in its housing. Some of Raf's sheep stopped grazing to regard him for a while, then resumed feeding. McLay had an uneasy smile, and his eyes switched furtively back and forth from Raf to me.

By the time Raf had finished, the veins in his forehead had subsided, and he wiped the sweat away with a sense of achievement. 'Never underestimate the perversity of objects,' he said. 'Never let them get away with it. A switch won't function, a fitting or tool won't work, then before you know — open revolt. Don't give an inch. Did you hear what I said, McLay? Never underestimate the perversity of objects.'

'I'd better be on my way now,' said McLay. There was an increasing air of placating wariness about him, as he realized the full extent of my brother's eccentricity.

'I'm going to use a windmill here,' said Raf. 'I should really have fitted one long ago. We're going to have to get back to wind power a lot more in this country.'

McLay rode back in the trailer without attempting to speak against the noise of the Norton, and when we reached the house he went off with a minimum leave-taking. 'An odd sort of chap. Didn't you think?' Raf said. There was no irony apparent in his voice.

Raf brought out more beer, and we sat again on the front step to drink it. The rural delivery car went past his gate without stopping. 'At Lincoln,' he said, 'the postman was a woman. She used to pedal about in yellow shorts, and her legs were very strong and brown.' He paused, and then said, 'So very brown', in a wistful way. 'She used to like me making puns about her having more mail than she could deal with. I have to go to Christchurch now.' The inconvenience of it rankled. 'I thought I might have had a letter from the Agriculture Department with information about goats,' he said. 'I intend those to be my two priorities this year; goats and the windmill.'

My brother's prevalent attitude to life was one of convinced cheerfulness, yet the non-arrival of the Department's letter concerning the goats, and the poignant recollection of the Lincoln post-girl's legs, had brought him as close to depression as I had ever seen him. The drink too, I suppose; we'd had quite a lot to drink. I felt it was a good time to tell him of my present. 'I brought you a present.'

'Thank you.'

'Cabernet Sauvignon. It's only New Zealand, but it's a medal winner, and four years old. I remembered you liked it best.'

The secret of Raf's joy in life was his appreciation of all the pleasures, irrespective of scale. He got up from the step in excitement. 'What a day!' he said. I got the bottle from my pack, and we had an uncorking ceremony. Raf put the bottle on the step to breathe and warm. 'We won't have any more beer now until after the wine,' he said. 'We don't want to be unable to appreciate it. Afterwards it doesn't matter.'

'I'll have to go at six, or seven. I don't want to have to hitch into Christchurch in the dark.'

'Right. I'd take you in, but I've only got one helmet, and the lights on the bike aren't going.'

Raf seemed to have forgotten his disappointment about the goats and other things; his thin face was alive with speculative enterprise again. 'What to have with the cabernet?' he said. 'We can't drink a good wine with just anything.' The full sophistication of a mind which had achieved honours in economics was given to the problem, and while the world grappled with the exigencies concerning inflation, corruption, guerilla warfare, spiritual degeneration and environmental pollution, Raf and I sat amidst his seventeen quiet hectares at West Melton, and discussed the entourage for our cabernet. My brother was a great believer in immediate things.

We had peas and baked potatoes, red tinned cabbage and corn. We ate it from plates on our knees, as we sat on the front step. Raf talked to me of his experiences on the continent, and how bad the *vin ordinaire* was in the south of France. He had some good wine glasses, and we raised them to the evening sun to admire the colour of the wine. Raf invited me to forget university, and join him on his goat and windmill farm. 'Economics is a subject that destroys an appreciation of spiritual things,' said Raf.

'Law. I'm doing law.'

'Same thing,' said Raf. 'Probably worse.' He became so carried away in trying to persuade me of the deadening nature of formal studies that he absent-mindedly kept the last of the cabernet sauvignon for himself, and so I fell back on beer. 'If you'd seen some of the places I have; Bangkok, Glasgow, Nice, then the value of privacy would be clear to you. Space brings the individual dignity, Tony. Herd animals are always the least attractive. Have you noticed that? I think that's one of the main reasons I want to move from sheep to goats. Goats have individuality, it seems to me.'

'A goat suits a name.'

'That's my point.' Raf sat relaxed on the step, his shingle land spreading away before him.

Just on twilight Raf took me down to the West Melton corner on the Norton. He drove carefully, conscious of the drink we'd had. 'Come out and see me soon,' he said. 'I meant what I said about forgetting economics, and joining me here to live.' I watched him ride off, without lights, and cautious of the power of the motor-bike. I could hear it long after he was out of sight, and I imagined my brother riding up his track, over the stones, towards his disreputable house. To resist the maudlin effects of the wine and the beer, I lay down in the long grass, out of sight of the road. I rested my head on my pack, and slept for an hour or so.

So I ended up hitch-hiking into the city in the dark after all. I was lucky though, for after walking a few minutes, I was picked up by a dentist and his daughter. Her name was Susan. We talked about cars. I tried not to breathe on Susan, lest she think me a typical boozy student. The dentist said he'd been having trouble trying to get the wheels balanced on his Lancia. 'Never underestimate the perversity of objects,' I said. The dentist liked that, and so did Susan. They had an appreciation for a turn of phrase. Raf would have enjoyed its reception, for incantations are rarely effective beyond the frontiers of their own kingdom.

Behind Stan's
1977
Egg Tempera on Gesso
360 x 710mm
Private Collection

Charlie's Tank
1977
Egg Tempera on Gesso
760 x 475mm
Collection: Robert McDougall Art Gallery, Christchurch

Private Bag
1977
Egg Tempera on Gesso
380 x 255mm
Collection: Roger & Dianne Hall, Auckland

CENTRAL OTAGO

Winter

No coddling. Chill winds
from the south and west
bring snow to the mountains,
snow and sleet to the valleys,
ice flashing its periodic
semaphore in the sun.

The earth resounds
under your feet. When
fog fills valleys
the mountains are
polar islands
in a grey-white sea.

And when log fires
burn long in the grate
the one thing
people share
is belief in spring.

At times it seems
you live in vast amphitheatres
surrounded by snow and ice,
suppressing a longing
for the heat of the summer sun,
for the land to stir again,
for the chance once more
to kneel on the waking earth
and feel the fresh grass
tingling beneath your grateful hands.

There is
no coddling.

Spring

Rivers fatten and bumble as
the snow melts, tumble down gorges,

spill out and over the flats. Buds harden,
swell; flowers return

and spring open, catch you unaware
like the first fierce shower

of spring rain. Soon, for orchardists,
it's frost-fighting sprays

and rankling, restless nights. There
is the elusive scent of blossom in the air,

birds are belligerent in the trees,
the land stirring like armies

breaking camp: the bugs are on
the move! It's a crazy season

where the private goes public
with the land's heady rubric.

Summer

Overhead the blue sky
is stretched
tight as a drum.

The hot summer sun
climbs slowly higher,
says, 'When I decline

you all decline.'
A lobster-legged farm boy
drives a puttering tractor

down the road, dust
billowing in the air.
Sheep graze paddocks

wide as generosity:
broom pods explode
with heat from the sun.

I lie on the grass
on the banks
of a water race

and look up into
total emptiness.
Would that I fill it

with all our dreams.

Autumn

Burnished, gold, Lombardy poplars line the
banks of streams. Bobbing leaves
glint in the afternoon sun, clear water
ripples over scoured and polished stones.

A rattling, mud-spattered truck
backfires, slows to a halt
outside the pub, duck feathers stuck
to the grille. 'Not my bloody fault,'

says the cocky, shouldering some locals
aside. Back on the high country farm
(the merinos, herefords and yokels
won't come to much harm)

sparrows hop and peck among the hens,
snicker and twitter in the trees
by scaly old hay barns.
A buff lone stag panics and flees

from a mob of raucous hunters
in a battered Land Rover.
Out front of his sod hut, the homestead's
whiskery latter-day drover

chops wood for the winter: chips
fly in the chaste air.
He feels the diffident grip
and ache of another year's

passing in his bones. In the late, serried
afternoon, tussock droops on the hill.
He goes inside leaving the axe buried
deep in wood. It is there still.

Limp Sock
1977
Egg Tempera on Gesso
600 x 510mm
Walker & Hall Collection, Auckland

49

Rozzie at Pisa
1978
Egg Tempera on Gesso
610 x 610mm
Collection: Artist

51

Shearer's Chair
1978
Watercolour
310 x 300mm
Collection: Artist

SALVATION'S ARMY

So easy the way
the river carries the sky
on its oiled shoulders
and tapering back,

the way light lies
like salvation,
or salvation's light;
so typical

the way that light
splinters whenever
an outsider
drops in.

It could be you
or me, obeying
an impulse or
seeking an out.

KYEBURN

The landscape only looks empty
as if no one, or nothing's
at home, for what, then,
is that sheer bright light

spilling like the cloud-cap
over the Kakanuis, doing
if it's not filling us up
as it makes the near and far

land buckle and glow, implying
you can't do without
the company of who or what's gone
along with what's coming up.

So good morning, sun.
No mutiny today. Destiny alone
will decide what survives
and be cared for, possibly.

TOWARDS THE MANIOTOTO

(after paintings by Grahame Sydney)

1

It all depends upon the way mood and mind
    conspire with panoply, technique
and murmurings of intent, instinctual
    determinations, or so one supposes,
painting out and crafting your responses
    to light and land, and a whole lot else
we haven't got names for. Selectivity's
    all when it comes to conveying aura
and the force of shapes and angles,
    the mystique of shadows.
                A painter's a composer,
an explorer, an architect: reconstruction
    and selection is what you live by,
discretion more than duplicity. Finally
    there's the entire world around us sieved
within us, the commentaries and inventions of a lifetime.

So if observation's the essence, emotion's the key,
    and meditation's a way in, back and forward
if we're to reflect where we are.
    This land en route to Middlemarch and beyond,
I know it well. It grows on those who strum
    the sight of tussock tuned by westerlies, thrumming
and humming, land that rolls and rolls
    from gully to gully like a series of giant
stepping stones for behemoths, country pecked
    by stony outcrops rising to tops
sprawling beneath the huge vault of sky.
    And days when clouds, blue-black and white,
sculpted and shaped like scoops of ice cream
    hang in the air above the ranges.

Darkness fills the valleys and the cloud bank
    known locally as the Taieri Pet
curves smooth and grainy like a boomerang
    over the Rock and Pillars. Wagons of cloud
are hauled north along the rim of the Lammerlaws
    and, further west, there's nothing but sky's
bravura colour making the far land glow.
    It only blossoms so – cerise, purple,
crimson and gold – because all but the memory is ending.

2

In the evening as darkness advances
    light on the river's more lasting,
more precious than that which emerges
    and clothes the earth as day burgeons.

Pools of the river, ponds in the valleys,
    earth's eyes that never close
reflecting light that venerates,
    will not be captured in the earth.
For light on water slaked from sky
    is inherent truth, a common language,
a manner of speaking for all that's lost
    for words. And the due process of painting's
neverending, to savour moments
    when light's accolades reassure us
there's always the prospect of beginnings
    for as long as the hulk of the world's between.

Thin Fires
1978
Egg Tempera on Gesso
540 x 680mm
Private Collection

Bannockburn
1979
Egg Tempera on Gesso
535 x 895mm
Private Collection

Weatherboards at Cluden
1979
Egg Tempera on Gesso
255 x 737mm
Private Collection

THE DUNGARVIE FESTIVAL

Ivan and Len worked together for two years, and then by chance got to know each other on the summer day they didn't make it to the Combined Local Bodies Civil Defence Seminar in Dunedin. Each council had to send two representatives, and there was a good deal of duck-shoving to sort out who had to go. Ivan was landed with it because he was a comparative newcomer, and wouldn't be missed anyway. To show that the council was taking Civil Defence seriously there had to be a chief as well as an Indian, so Len, who was Administration Officer, had to go.

He came around early to pick Ivan up, so that they could be away in good time, and Ivan saw that they had been given the oldest vehicle in the fleet. They would be the Kettles come to town in Dunedin. The ute's left front guard had been in pink undercoat for years, and in the back was an assortment of road signs and three boxes of poisoned carrots that someone kept forgetting to set out around the treatment ponds. Low on both doors were paint bubbles, showing where the rust was eating through from the inside.

Len knew he looked incongruous. His good suit was already picking up a variety of rubbish from the wool sack which covered the front seat. Neither of them said anything about the ute though, and Len drove as befitted a chief, and Ivan sat on the pink wing side as the Indian. Len's manila envelope with the programme for the seminar lay on top of the dash, so Ivan put his there as well. They didn't discuss the programme: it had headings such as statutory responsibilities of local authorities, and counter-disaster logistics for rural communities.

Reticent, I suppose, is a word that you could use for Len, and professional would be another. He did his job from day to day without malice, or favour, and without any inclination to pry into the thoughts, or lives, of colleagues. A working relationship over two years had for Ivan merely confirmed those aspects of Len's nature

that he had recognised within the first week.

'We've drawn the short straws,' said Len with a smile.

'It looks that way.'

That's all they said for a while, but to be fair to both of them the ute didn't encourage conversation. The motor laboured and the road signs and poisoned carrots in the back had a disappointing fellowship. Also there was the threat of the Central summer, even at that time of the day. The ground had little cover, and the schist outcrops were bright, scaly, with no sweat to give.

'I don't much like the sound of the old girl,' said Len when they were close to Dungarvie, and as if by speaking of it he gave recognition, even acquiescence, the motor sickened in that instant, and then died. They drifted, with just the road noise and the diminished quarrel of the road signs and carrots, almost to the restricted speed zone of the village, and where they should have reduced speed the ute stopped completely.

'Ah well, Jesus,' said Len.

'At least we're not far from a garage. That's a welcome fluke.'

'That's true.'

There was a garage at Dungarvie. They could see it clearly. In fact all of Dungarvie could be clearly seen ahead: on the left the garage, then a community hall, on the right three stock crates jacked up on a section until needed, then the gap of a lucerne paddock before the store. Past the store was the only separate house they could see for all Dungarvieites. Len tried the starter several times without success, then went to the front of the ute and looked at the engine, more from a sense of responsibility than any hope of finding what was wrong. Ivan stood by him, but looked along the flat road to Dungarvie. He saw no one; nothing moved, and in the time between the ute stopping and their walk to the garage beginning, only a blue Triumph passed them, paying no heed to them, or the restricted speed zone, disappearing down the road before they had taken many steps.

Len and Ivan took off their ties, and folded them and put them in the pockets of the coats they carried as they walked into Dungarvie. 'I suppose I should have rung up the yard yesterday and insisted on a better vehicle,' said Len. 'I just never thought we'd end up with that ute. I mean they knew we were going through to a meeting in Dunedin. It's poor.'

'I suppose it's mostly bad luck really.' Ivan was more accustomed to being given the ute as council transport.

'Yes, but after all we are going to the city as representatives of the council, aren't we.'

Ivan could feel his lips drying as he walked. He licked them, and moved his coat from his shoulder where it was making him sweat, and let it hang over his wrist. Through the thin soles of his best shoes he could feel the unevenness of the seal. It seemed to take a long time to walk the two hundred metres or so before the garage. Some barley grass heads had attached themselves to his trouser legs. He felt his face screwing up against the glare of the sun.

The garage was wooden; so old and so high that it may once have been a smithy. There was no one amid its work-day untidiness, although a transistor radio, hidden like a cicada in the jumble of the side bench, sang on. Ivan and Len were not surprised. They knew that in a country district one mechanic is thinly spread. They kept walking and even before they reached the hall, the sound of laughter claimed them: laughter despite the few, quiet buildings and the sky burnt to a powder blue. The laughter billowed from the community hall, but then lost its force in all the calm, surrounding space. Laughter at once natural and engaging, asking to be found out, yet also with defiance perhaps at all that emptiness, all that press of the given moment which there was no movement to disguise.

The hall was representative of a persistent species: outside all cream weatherboards and bleached red tin roof, inside a wooden floor with chairs stacked to one side, and on the walls the district rolls of honour for the Great War 1914-18 and the Second World War 1939-45. At the far end was one door to the committee room, and another, plus a slide, to the 'facilities'. A rolled bowling mat leaned like a furled flag in a corner, and on top of chair stacks were three jars of dried flowers and an unclaimed cardigan.

The laughter came from the far end of the hall, in the open door of the facilities, but Len and Ivan found it difficult to see the people there at first because of the alternate shadow, then the fierce shafts of light from the windows, as they walked the length of the floor. Two women and a man sat on chairs and peeled potatoes. One woman had yellow shorts, matching sneakers and the ease of attractiveness; the other had a floral dress and a laugh like a string of firecrackers. Their helper was a Maori, very thin, wearing a green, army singlet, shorts and heavy boots. Even carrying their coats and ties Ivan and Len felt over-dressed. The three had a sack of potatoes and two enamel basins at their feet. They washed and peeled the potatoes in one basin and laid them in the water of the other so they wouldn't brown.

Ivan and Len had found their mechanic it turned out — Charles. Evonne had the Hollywood legs, and Judith the laugh which made every speaker feel a wit. The two of them were mother helpers for a guide camp being held in the domain next to the hall. It is the way sometimes that the more random the meeting, the more relaxed the mood. They all fitted in; there was not a nark amongst them. By rights they should never have met up at all. Ivan and Len should have been on their way to the seminar in Dunedin, should have been through Dungarvie too quickly to have heard the laughter from the hall, or to have seen the red crosses by the names of soldiers who had fallen. Yet Ivan could smell the bowling mats, and old paper lining cupboards, see the withered flowers in their jars, and the table tennis challenge ladder which displayed its champion so aptly as C. Meek.

Ivan sat with Evonne and Judith, offered himself as a replacement potato peeler, while Charles and Len went back to examine the ute. 'Does it matter much if you're late getting to Dunedin?' asked Evonne.

'We're supposed to be going to a civil defence meeting.'

'I don't know much about civil defence,' said Evonne, 'but then I don't know much about Girl Guide camps either, yet I'm here.'

'All camps have certain fundamentals, like peeling potatoes.' Ivan was flattered by Judith's laugh into imagining he had made a joke. She threw a potato into the basin with such force that the droplets as they scattered were caught in the sun from the window and for an instant held all the colours of the rainbow within themselves. Judith and Evonne began their story of all the indiscretions and mistakes they had committed as mother helpers, and of the Guide Officers who never failed to discover them. As Charles, Len and Ivan held no rank within Guides they were seen as reassuring envoys from a more tolerant world.

Carrots had replaced potatoes by the time Len and Charles returned, and Ivan had joined in so completely that the other men returning had to break the circle. 'Charles says it will take a while: probably something electrical,' Len said.

'Could be the distributor,' said Charles. Judith laughed and Evonne joined in. 'Heh,' said Charles, 'I've told you before there's nothing the matter with my name. I bet plenty of mechanics are called Charles.'

'How many Maori ones?' said Evonne. Judith's laugh, so sudden and so complete, drew them all in. Afterwards Charles looked at Len and Ivan. He tried to make his thin face deadpan.

'These women are trying to offend me,' he said.

'I rang the office,' said Len.

'What do they think?' asked Ivan.

'Well, they want us to go on if we can be on the road again before midday, otherwise we might as well wait here and bring the ute back when it's fixed. Someone would only have to be driven over to get it anyway.'

'Right.'

'I'll tow her in and have a look at things now,' said Charles. 'If you come up in an hour or so I should know what the story is.' He took a carrot from Evonne's hand, as if she should know better than to grip such a thing, and walked back through the hall. His shoulder blades showed clearly under the singlet, and his boots seemed clumsy on the ends of such thin legs.

'Goodbye Charles,' said Judith sweetly. He didn't turn at their laughter, but waggled his fingers with his hand behind his back.

As a break from the vegetables, Len and Ivan were taken through the back door of the hall to be shown the camp. There were no goalposts on the domain because of summer, but at the far end some pony-jumps were still set up, and on the hall side two lines of bell tents with a flag-pole in between. Ivan thought the scene like a limited budget set for a Boer War movie, with a minimum authenticity of the grass worn between the two rows of off-white tents, the flag-pole, the heat shimmer beginning over the brown landscape, and the blue, hollow infinity of the sky. He thought things might look like that at the end of the world: all people spirited away and just the props, the objects, left to get on with it.

'Where are they all?' said Len.

'They're on a badge trek in the hills. A six-hour round hike from the dropping off point and they have to carry their lunch and emergency clothing in case the weather turns. All the qualified people have gone with them, and we're left here to prepare tea,' said Judith, 'and look after Suzie Allenton who was sick last night and is sleeping now in her tent.'

'We're supposed to make an inspection of the tents sometime during the day,' said Evonne, 'and give points to the tidy ones which go towards the top tent competition.'

Ivan was about to ask what happened if the Boer commandos attacked while the camp was undefended, but he remembered he had said nothing to the others about the impression the tents had created. Yet he imagined Botha's or de Wet's horsemen cantering in to surprise the mother helpers and sick, sleeping Suzie Allenton. 'Were you ever in the Scouts, Ivan?' said Len from the back steps of the hall.

'No.'

'It wasn't my thing either. I never had anything to do with Scouts or Boys' Brigade, and although I was roped into National Service the only tents I remember were bivouac things which we had to carry ourselves. They were so small you had to crawl into them.'

'Time for your confessions now,' said Ivan to Judith and Evonne.

'I was brought up on a farm,' said Judith. 'I could never be in group things.'

'I was in the city, but don't remember going to Brownies, Guides, or anything like that. I don't think anybody ever invited me.' Evonne looked carefully at the tents and flag-pole, as if for the first time. 'Have I missed out on something important do you think?'

'You can do your penance as mother helper,' said Len. 'Girl Guides, like any other army, march on their stomachs.'

'I'd like to march on the stomachs of a few of them,' said Judith.

The direct sunlight was intense. Len's head lolled back to rest against the door jamb, and his eyes closed. The others rested their heads in their hands, and supported both by propping their elbows on their knees. Ivan wished he had a hat, and found himself breathing through his mouth. 'Should we make a round of the tents now?' said Evonne after a time. The two women lifted their heads enough to see across the grass to the tents, and assessed the effort it would take to visit them all, and compared that with whatever energy and duty they felt.

'Maybe later,' said Judith.

'I'll just check on Suzie then,' said Evonne. She stood up, pulled her shorts down at the back of her thighs, and walked across grass so dry that it crunched beneath her sneakers.

'I could sleep the day away in a tent myself,' said Len. 'The less you do the less you want to do.'

'She's a good sort,' said Judith, watching Evonne as she neared the tents. 'Her husband's wealthy, but she's still come to take her turn. She pitches in just like everybody else. She even cleaned up on the bus when one of the girls was sick after fish and chips. It's not very pleasant then in the confined space of a bus when you're travelling so far.' Ivan and Len watched Evonne at the tents; her banana shorts and sneakers, her graceful, brown legs. The men kept their faces non-committal in Judith's presence, and they made no comment. 'Yes,' said Judith. 'Beaut legs. She's lucky there, don't you think? Mine keep getting thicker year by year.' She pulled her dress up to show her strong legs and big knees with a smiling crease on each. 'What about your legs?' she said to Ivan.

'Skinny and hairy. Not a pretty sight.'

'It's just as well we're both wearing longs,' said Len. 'I've nothing much to offer in the way of legs either.'

'Charles's have a good natural tan, but they're skinny too,' said Judith.

'Evonne will have to win first prize for legs then,' said Ivan. Evonne looked back towards the hall, and laid her head to one side on her hands to show that Suzie Allenton was still sleeping.

Len and Ivan didn't wait for Evonne to reach them across the domain, but gave a wave and told Judith that they might be back if

Charles wasn't able to fix the truck in time.

'Oh, god,' she said. 'Do come back and rescue us.'

'We haven't lost a mother helper yet,' Len said.

Once the habitual responsibility for events had been shifted from him by forces beyond his control, Len became increasingly relaxed. He was in no hurry on their walk back to the garage, and he talked with Ivan of seeing the original sub-division plan of Dungarvie in the council files: two hundred private sections had been surveyed in the flush of colonial enthusiasm, and sites for shops and churches, but even the gold rushes didn't create that Dungarvie, didn't build its churches, or fill its cemeteries. Dungarvie had never been much more than they could see. Ivan noted that there was not even a pub in the place, and his interest was not historical. At least the high, red barn of the garage offered some shade.

'She's never been any Rolls Royce,' said Charles when they joined him. 'However you shouldn't have any trouble getting to Dunedin and back.' Len and Ivan looked without enthusiasm at the ute, its patch of pink undercoat, soft tyres, and stains weeping from the various rust spots on the body. The carrots in the back were bleached and wrinkled, a sign face-up announced road works ahead. Len thought of the drive to Dunedin in the heat, and the attention that would be drawn to them by their late arrival at the seminar. 'On the other hand,' said Charles as one of life's entrepreneurs, 'we could declare a Dungarvie Festival if you wanted to stay for a while, and give Evonne and Judith some company. I've even got a carton of beer that we could all chip in on.'

Len opened his mouth as if to say no in his role as Administration Officer, but then was seized by the wonderful implausibility of it all as he stood in the garage doorway. The few ill-hung bell tents he could see not blocked by the hall, the dozing store, the barley grass in the free sections, the sheep crates with dung burnt to an inoffen-sive crust, the old smithy garage he stood in, Charles smiling from the shadows which matched his skin. 'Well why not,' Len said, and having said it and not been struck down by conscience, or by lightning, he repeated it boldly. 'Well why not. We're too late to bother going on anyway, don't you think?'

'Yes,' said Ivan and Charles with certainty. Charles hoisted the carton of beer into the back of the truck, and they drove back slowly towards the hall through the welling shimmer of the road and grass.

The mother helpers had gone inside again, and were preparing a vat of mince and onion to go with the potatoes. The sight of the beer on Charles's shoulder was enough to start them laughing. The sooner the meal was prepared, the sooner they could relax, Judith said, so Ivan and Len chopped carrots directly into the mince while Charles sliced onions. Tears ran down his face, and his brows lifted oddly as he tried to keep his eyes from closing.

'Come on, come on,' said Charles. The women took some apples and apricots, everyone took a mug, and Charles led the way across the domain to the culvert where the road crossed the stream. There was a small, scoured pool where the concrete ended. Charles took the bottles of beer from the carton, and dropped them on to the shingle bottom, reaching down till his shoulder was in the water so that the bottles would land gently. Part of his singlet became bright again with the water, and the drops skated across the oil of his hands. There were small grasshoppers at the pool's edge, and a silver skink for a moment on the concrete of the culvert bridge. Len tasted his share of the first bottle, which was given no time to cool.

'I love the salty taste good beer has,' he said. 'Ah, it's needed in this weather.'

They surrounded the small pool. Len and Judith stepped over the trickle of its outlet and sat on the other side, but that put them hardly any further apart than the others. All of them were soon barefoot.

Charles's feet were dainty alongside his work boots. Judith tucked her floral dress up like pantaloons, and hung her legs in the water so that the effect of refraction had them broken at the calf. Ivan leaned forward to eat a ripe apricot so that the juice would fall on to the grass, and not his best shirt, or suit trousers. He had knotted the corners of his handkerchief, soaked it, and it lay on his dark head as a first defence from the sun. Occasionally a truck, or car, went by in the midday heat. The growing whine of any approach gave all five a chance to compose their faces. Sometimes drivers, or passengers, happened to look down and saw with envy, surprise, or condescension the group around the culvert pool celebrating the festival of Dungarvie. But as time went on, the road, its travellers, its starting points and destinations, ceased to be a relevant awareness, and no disguise, or provision, for them was made at all.

'Let's hope no one breaks down,' said Evonne to Charles, 'otherwise you'd have to leave our picnic and fix the car.'

'Actually I never meant to be a mechanic,' he said. 'I wanted to be a physicist.'

Judith's laugh exploded pod-like in the dry air. She had difficulty in holding her mug of beer. Len's laugh was almost as loud, almost as distinctive; high-pitched and abrupt, it was not the social laugh that Ivan had heard from him in the past, but a new laugh. It was a laugh of instinctive delight and lack of inhibition. 'No, I did, fair go,' said Charles. Laughter feeds on itself, so that they were all drawn in. Charles himself found his voice so collapsed with laughter that it was husky when he managed to carry on. 'Look, look, I was a marvel at physics at school, and could have easily gone on, but at Vic I got side-tracked into a heavy metal band, and lost my bursary because I failed everything except physics.'

What a depth of humour and irony there is in actuality. Evonne lay back because her stomach was sore from laughing. There must be a hundred reasonable ways to explain the move from physics and a Wellington rock band to sole charge of the Dungarvie garage in the old smithy. It had the freakish likelihood of truth. 'I wanted to be a wildlife officer,' said Len, sudden in his decision to be confidential as well. He had dipped his hands into the pool, and cooled his face with the water. The hair of his forehead was stuck together. 'I wanted to save the black robin, the takahe, the kakapo and so on.' At his ears amid the short sideburns were the first grey hairs, and on the sides of his nose the sheen where his glasses normally rested. 'More than anything else that's what I was set on doing, and somehow I've ended up as an accountant; a Council Administration Officer.' He was still sufficiently self-conscious to add that of course he had remained a financial member of the Forest and Bird Society. It set the others off again, particularly Judith. She considered it a great one-liner. Her feet jerked beneath the water and her laughter cracked like a stock-whip across the domain. Did any accountant ever dream of becoming an accountant, any more than the day-shift foreman of the chicken nugget factory dreamt of his success, or a man sold his soul to the devil for the right to be caretaker at the Shangri-La Lodge and Cabin Park? How many shopping reporters, high school language teachers, rural delivery drivers, one term politicians, or Pleasant Valley inmates could point to a constant ambition?

The bottles of beer lay on the gravel bottom of the pool, and quivered like trout in the ripple of Judith's feet. The stones had a fuzz of slime because the water was barely flowing, the label from one bottle had come adrift and undulated like a fin. The pool had a thin lip of green cress and clover before the brown grass began. 'How can you work day after day in this heat?' said Evonne to Charles, who was reaching down into the pool to bring up another prize.

'You tell me,' he said. 'This part of the country is stranger to me than to most of you, I'd say. I'm Tuhoe you see, children of the mist, and so on. This isn't my place.' It was a final incongruity. Len was delighted with it.

'I don't suppose there are many Tuhoe physicists in Dungarvie when you come to think of it,' he said.

Everything seemed amusing to them in that afternoon. Sometimes there is an intoxication of the heart which has little to do with drink: some combination of circumstances and personalities which slips past defences and brings a mood of goodwill and acceptance. All of which may be just another way of saying how hot it was in Central that day, how influential the beer and fruit on empty stomachs, how each person felt release in a new role and company knowing it was just for one day. Ivan noticed that Len rolled his trousers higher as time went on, and that his face at times was almost impetuous. They had left the office, yet not arrived at the seminar. They had shrugged off routine, yet not assumed interim responsibility. They were in a pleasant limbo, and yet with some excuse.

'Me?' Evonne was saying. 'I wanted to be a school dental nurse and make snowmen with red ink faces from cotton wool wads. The uniform quite suited me I thought, and as well you had your own special room. Instead I'm just a rich bitch I suppose.'

'A toast to the mother helpers,' said Charles amid the talk of Bertie Germ and money, and the mother helpers drank deeply to themselves as a sign that they recognised their worth.

Ivan wondered about himself; what he had intended as distinct from what he had become. The physicist, the wildlife ranger, the dental nurse, and Judith still with her mystery, all wanted to hear of his lost life. Judith shaded her eyes the better to watch him, and her mouth was open for her explosive, benevolent laugh. 'An actor,' he said. There was joy that he had not disappointed them. Charles threw his head back as if to dislodge something in his throat. 'I did a fair bit at school, and then a Polytech course. We had a group that toured

schools and hospitals, but when the funding was withdrawn I switched to office management.' As he said it, he was amazed how the exigencies of the moment become in retrospect a seamless process of inevitable selection.

'Oh, but you would have been good on the stage,' said Evonne loyally. 'You could be a gentleman caller for Laura, or a rebel in a kitchen-sink play.'

'Or the fool in Lear,' said Len, 'who knows more than the king.'

'Give us something now,' said Judith.

'I've forgotten it all.'

'Yes, come on Ivan,' said Len. He was delighted that his colleague had revealed such an exotic past. A chant began.

'We want Ivan. We want Ivan.'

In any other setting, any other time, or people, Ivan would have suspected an edge of vindictiveness, an underlying hope of some humiliation, but the Dungarvie Festival was all goodwill. None of them knew each other well enough to wish for any harm. Ivan stood up to free his breathing, and gave them one of Biff's speeches from *Death of a Salesman* about the dangerous gap between self-image and reality.

As part of his concentration on it, Ivan had an exact awareness of the others listening, their combined physical existence on the grass there, around the culvert pool. A grass stem turned in Len's fingers, and on one pale ankle bone a blue-green vein was looped. Judith's sunburnt face was full on to him to give support, and Charles nodded as he listened and dabbed an insect from his beer. The Boer War tents were in their two rows at a distance, the hall and store and garage becalmed in heat and time. Then Ivan quoted Willie to his friends in the Dungarvie domain; isolated from the rest of the world with a bird singing up high somewhere, one great, strutted pylon glinting on the hill, two lines of sagging tents, and in one of them somewhere, sick, sleeping Suzie Allenton whom he never saw.

Ivan had his immediate appreciation however, and a stock truck happened to pass at just that time and made a roar of approval upon the little bridge above them. Judith had seen the film version, and talked of it with Len and Evonne, while Charles gave Ivan his ideas on the importance of sustaining enthusiasms. Ivan was breathing heavily because of the heat and his nervousness at reciting. He was content to listen for a while. 'You must keep the idea of your life being special,' Charles said. 'Of it having nothing to do with any historical generalisations, or social trends, but instead as a free-wheeling thing with all the possibilities still there if you want to explore them.'

'There's an underlying feeling of time past,' Ivan heard Judith saying, 'and it's pressing forward into the present and the future more and more.' For a moment Ivan thought that Charles would accept that as an answer in their own conversation, but Charles still waited.

'Sometimes I doubt the depth of what we see,' said Ivan. 'Sometimes despite the exact, connecting detail before us, I feel it bulging, and just a shimmer at the seams to hint of things quite different beneath.'

'That's it,' said Charles, and he topped another bottle.

'Didn't he marry Marilyn Monroe or something?' asked Len. 'I thought I read that he married Marilyn Monroe.' He picked blemishes from his apple with his fingernail.

'At our last staff meeting,' said Ivan, 'we were discussing the computer training programme, and for an uneasy moment the words spoken didn't fit the movements of the people's mouths, and there was the scent of the open sea that I haven't thought of for years.'

'That's it,' said Charles. 'Last week I took an irrigation pump I'd mended back to a cockie up the valley, and at the gate a dog challenged me. Not a sheepdog either, but a Labrador. The sun was go-ing down and this old dog stood right before me, barking hoarsely but it had so little belief in its own threat, or mine, that its eyes turned away as it barked. I had a feeling that it marked something in my life, but I had no way of guessing the significance.'

'Kerouac called Monroe a trash blonde. He met her once and she snubbed him,' said Evonne.

'I've never read any Kerouac,' said Len. 'I come across the name from time to time, but I've never read anything.'

'We'll do our Kerouac dance for you,' Judith said. She and Evonne stood up and swung their hips slowly, and undulated their arms. Judith's dress was still tucked in, and her legs were pink with sunburn, only behind the knees still white. Evonne could have been a Marilyn Monroe herself, with smooth muscles on her thighs, and heavy breast. Len gave his new, high-pitched laugh, but much softer than before.

'That's just a hula,' he said.

'Now reincarnation is another thing,' said Charles. The beer had reached his eyes and they had a moist gleam. He lifted the strap of his green singlet, and scratched his shoulder. His thin body was crumpling in the heat and the relaxation of unforced conversation. 'I find myself considering it quite often.'

'You believe in reincarnation?' said Ivan. Evonne and Judith still did their Kerouac dance, and Len clapped in time. It was a leisurely dance because of the heat, and Judith could drink from her mug without interrupting her movement.

'Let me give you an example,' said Charles. 'I had this dream of hunting polar bears from a kayak, and one reared up on an icefloe and I felt all the authenticity of detail in an instant: how the water drummed the kayak's skin against my hips, and the bear's fur yellowed and disordered in the arm-pits as it raised great paws.'

'An Eskimo dream. You didn't,' said Ivan.

'What's this?' said Evonne.

'Charles dreamt he was an Eskimo.' The dancing was over and Evonne and Judith sat down to laugh again.

'You didn't!' said Len.

'Only a few nights ago,' said Charles. 'It was so true that it woke me up. It took a while for the Arctic chill to pass. I got out of bed and went to the window. I could see some of the hill facings full to the moonlight, and a fence-line across them. But there wasn't a polar bear in sight.'

'Perhaps an Eskimo has had a vision of Dungarvie as recompense,' said Ivan. 'The view from your window with the dark gullies and moonlit tussock slopes of the Old Man Range, and a single fence-line to divide one side of emptiness from the other.'

'Or the festival now,' said Judith. 'Us at our picnic here when we're all supposed to be somewhere else. But it's so hot. You'd hardly dream such heat.'

Even reincarnation and the Kerouac dance couldn't protect them all forever. The afternoon was well on, and consciences were stirring. No one voiced it, but they had a small fear that the Guides and qualified instructors might return from training and they would have to see themselves reflected in scornful eyes — five feckless people, moist faced and idle in the sun from an excess of goodwill and beer.

'I suppose we'll have to go,' said Len, but he continued to lie back, his suit trousers rolled below the knees. 'I haven't enjoyed myself so much in ages.'

'We've still got our inspection to do, and poor Suzie Allenton,' said Evonne.

'And the meal,' said Judith.

'You didn't give the mother helpers any of the carrots from the truck did you, Charles?'

'Why not?'

'They're poisoned.' Len knew this would set Judith off again.

'That's the sort of lunch issue our council runs to,' said Ivan. Amid the laughter, Len clumsily stood up, but was unable to find his balance. Too many factors were combined against him; dizziness from standing up suddenly in the heat, pins and needles in his left leg from the hard ground, the flattery of beer and laughter, the loss of steadying inhibitions. He began to fall sideways despite whirling his arms, and the laughter increased. He tried to turn his fall into a leap across the pool, easy enough, but hit the far edge with an outstretched leg and half fell in. Had it meant his death, the others could not have stopped their laughter, which went on as Len hobbled in a circle on the grass to get his jarred leg moving properly again.

The incident allowed Ivan and Len to make easy goodbyes, with no scrutiny of the day attempted. Laughter and spontaneous acceptance had been the start of their trivial festival, with laughter and openness they kissed and parted.

Ivan and Len carried their shoes across the domain, and when they reached the truck they opened both doors, but stood outside for a while until the cab was a little less stifling. 'You'd better drive,' said Len. 'I think you drank less than me.' They could see Charles fitting his heavy boots as they pulled away, and when Ivan gave a farewell on the horn, Charles, Evonne and Judith raised their hands, and even at that distance and above the noise of the ute, there seemed an echo of machine-gun fire which might have been Judith's laugh.

Dungarvie fell over the edge of the world behind them; soon they could see just the top of the high smithy garage. The morning's trip seemed a life away. 'We're not much further ahead on civil defence,' said Ivan.

'The farmers around here say that disaster struck some time ago anyway, and today's seminar was too late for that.' Len was dusting his feet with his socks while Ivan drove, then he rolled down the legs of his suit trousers and began picking out spears of barley grass. 'I never knew you'd been an actor,' he said. 'We should see more of each other and talk about those things.'

'We will.'

'Judith was the only one that didn't tell us what she wanted to be. Did you hear her say that she was going through a break-up with her husband?'

'No.'

'She told me while you were talking to Charles about reincarnation, or his time at Vic, or maybe his Eskimo dreams. Being a mother helper was a chance to step back from normal things and sort herself out.'

'She could laugh anyway.'

'That's true. You meet interesting people by accident at times, don't you. Scores of times I must have been through Dungarvie and I don't think I've ever stopped. Yet today was some sort of fun wouldn't you say?'

They talked easily in the afternoon sun. The Dungarvie Festival had been one of those oddities — a oncer — like a freak, giant hail storm, or the escape of zoo leopards into the suburbs. Those things which happen once in a blue moon, and which bind those caught up in them with a sharp sense of comradeship, and of life's possibilities after all.

VAN MORRISON IN CENTRAL OTAGO

Take me back to the days
before rock and roll,
Life with Dexter and
the Goons, days when
Dad and Dave still bumbled
in Snake Gully
and the skies were not
cloudy all day, before

I saw tussock, heard it
speaking in tongues
and chanting with the westerly:
What's productive here
is what's in your heart,
sworn through your eyes,
ears, the flitter of the
wind in your hair;

the smell, the taste
of air from the mountains,
off flats where the river
runs from somewhere north
to somewhere south and the sky's
forever. It's not picturesque,
it's essential, almost
grand, and it aches

like the rhythms of truth
scornful of tittle-tattle.
You have to be here, you
have to feel the deep
slow surge of the hills,
the cloak of before, the wrench
of beyond. You know
what, you know

not. And that's what
makes it heart-stopping,
articulate, hurtful
like resuscitation.
You cannot bear to use
the word again again
when driven by an urge
to begin to begin.

Auripo Road
1979
Egg Tempera on Gesso
420 x 748mm
Collection: Jocelyn & Cliff Broad, Invercargill

C L O U D S

And something like that
they floated over in the evening
on a westerly, drifting
and the boy said
They're like yokels
in a field of cut corn
and my friend said
What's he referring to?
and I said, Clouds, look
and he said, By joves, amazing
how did he think of that?
and I said, Don't ask me
ask him, so he did
and the boy, shrugged

Huntaway Hut
1980
Egg Tempera on Gesso
395 x 495mm
Collection: Mr & Mrs F. K. Wardell, Christchurch

Dogtrials Room
1980
Egg Tempera on Gesso
500 x 830mm
Private Collection

WATCH FOR THE ICE

for Jo Hansen

Here one day, gone the next:
nothing unusual in that. The earth
caught in the grip of winter,

wet hibernation. But very much alive,
as we are alive and the blood
quickens when clouds blow over

and the sun shines on bare trees
and frosty grass … unashamed
celebration of the pastoral,

embodying a wish to live unwished
and without concern for rewards.
Ah, if it were that simple.

We forget what we want to
remember: the demons batter the glass.
Watch for the ice; watch for the ice

as you go, speculative, loosening, essential …

Marquee at the Dogtrials
1982
Watercolour
200 x 455mm
Collection: A. Dickens, Christchurch

ON THE EDGE OF A MEADOW

The tree is complete in a cloak of green.
    I stare for hours
at the lamps of stored summer light,
        and shiver.
    They promise too much
      when too much is incomplete.

A dead tree's branches
    are like a ladder leaning on the sky.
The breeze is a paw at my face:
    it fondles the grass
        and passes on.

And the lamps are the lights
      of happiness
  meant for when we discover
    what the world could be.

A PROCESSION OF CLOUDS

There's no adamance in them, all's
inconclusive; the seemingly
most persistent lift, rent, skedaddle,
and always at something else's behest:
there's compliance for you.

Then comes sky and more sky
and all the colours of pageantry.

Sky music's phrasing
is extra-terrestrial, its rhythms
more ethereal until clouds rumble
and thunder peels and lightning's
a slashing swordfish
reminding you that sky's
an ocean and vice versa.

In the evening a procession
of clouds goes by,
festival floats
draped and decked in ribbons and flowers.
Their messages read
All's the word for one last hope
and even that's inconclusive.

But look, there are clouds
like tubas shining
and the stratus are striped
like braided trousers
stepping out from horizon to horizon
of the longest boulevard in the world.

Dog Water
1982
Watercolour
330 x 225mm
Private Collection

Killing House
1983
Egg Tempera on Gesso
600 x 600mm
Collection: Manawatu Art Gallery, Palmerston North

AFTERNOON

Calm and still as water in a well
the afternoon
works quietly on

the wind
having fainted and died
on its way here

The willows
lean out over the river
as in prayer

birds are singing
as if for the last time
and I lie

like a stranded fish
belly up in the grass
hoping

listening for the words to our song

Twilight on the Maniototo
1985
Egg Tempera on Gesso
712 x 968mm
Collection: Pamela R. Williams, Christchurch

BODY AND SOUL

The snow had become water on the quiet road, yet alongside in the tussock grass it lay like separate white handkerchiefs. In the folds of the tussock hills there were still sweeps and angles of it etched by the sun over the contours of the land. The tussock was a rough coat over the hills, and only the road cut through it.

In the first hour after leaving the town they talked a good deal, the easy shorthand of husband and wife, but as the car worked higher into the hills Vicky became quiet; only smiling in reply to the things her husband said. She watched the tussock and the snow as if there were more than a world of tussock and snow passing. Her hands rested softly like birds in her lap, with the rings as bands upon them.

'I told you about George Liddell and the Dunedin branch,' said Paul, and Vicky smiled, but didn't turn her head towards him. 'It's a pleasant function of the position, to be able to tell George that. Being able to give people what they deserve even in a modest business way has a lot of satisfaction. That Sydney trip. I'll have to be away all week I'm afraid.' He whistled for a time as he drove. 'What do you bet Simon has forgotten we're coming today, aye? Wouldn't that be just typical.' Paul rested his hand on her dress. He wanted to cheer her up. She turned and smiled.

'It wouldn't surprise me. We know he's not practical at all.'

'Right. Like even forgetting what day it is. I hate to think of him in business.'

'So do I.'

'It can't be far.' He began looking for any signs that they were close. 'All looks very much the same, this country,' he said. The tussock was a rough coat over the hills, and only the road cut through it. Paul looked across to his wife, and she looked out on to tussock and snow. Because she was quiet and looked sad, he leant over and cupped his free hand over one of the hands like birds in her lap. 'Happy?' he said.

Simon's bach was quite new. He rented it from a Dunedin doctor whose love of solitude had died once it was consummated. The bach sat above the road, and faced north for the winter sun. There were two concrete water tanks like pill boxes beside it, and Simon's motorbike was draped with sacks on the small verandah. For miles there was no other building. 'This is his Walton's Mountain,' said Paul as they turned off the road, and he and Vicky laughed. Simon came to the door; stood grinning as they drove to within a few feet of him.

'What kept you? I thought you might have arrived last night,' he said. There was snow in the south shadow of the bach.

'Shopping,' said Paul. He cocked his thumb at his wife, and rolled his eyes upwards. By stressing the idiosyncrasy of women, he suggested a bond between men.

'Ah,' said Simon. He took two of the cases inside. 'I had a bit of a clean up,' he said. 'I meant to do more, but I began painting again and didn't get time.' It was Vicky's turn to lift her eyes. 'You know how it is,' Simon said. He had made up the two single beds, and pushed them together in a clumsy but touching effort to represent his idea of how husband and wife should be. There was only one bedroom, and Simon had taken a lilo and sleeping bag to the studio.

'You've had a fair fall of snow,' said Paul.

'A fair bit yesterday. In the afternoon a good deal of it.'

To be brothers is no guarantee of intimacy, or understanding, yet each smiled at the other's similar face; willing to be a friend, and willing it to be so. Time had given them different priorities, and only superficial things and recollections were left for them in common. 'I use rock gas for the cooking and hot water,' said Simon. As if it needed proof he opened the cupboard by his sink, and they looked at the rock gas cylinder plainly there. 'Rock Gas' it said on it, sure enough.

'We use rock gas in our caravan. Never had any trouble with it at all. Have we darling?'

'No,' she said. She was a beautiful woman.

'I've had no trouble with it,' said Simon. His voice began to yawn although his mouth remained the same.

'I'd say these rock gas people have built up a tidy business.'

They went walking after lunch. Nowhere did they come to any fences, and the only one Paul could remember was that which followed the road. Simon seemed not to care how far they walked. They talked, and went on and on, keeping just below the spur lines to avoid the breeze. They climbed almost to the top of one of the highest hills. 'It's called Saviour's Hill,' said Simon. The tussock was too damp to sit on, but they crouched down and looked over the lesser hills lit by the cool sun; looked down and over the plain. Whenever the air moved they could feel the cold. The snow that had been there in the morning was nearly gone, but it had chilled the hills in its departure.

'What do you do? When you're not painting, what do you do?' asked Paul. Simon looked down, and smiled. It was a smile not of amusement, but wry recognition. As though he had told himself that Paul would ask that question, and yet he couldn't help but think less of his brother for doing it. In its way it was a question which proved the completeness of Paul's misunderstanding.

'Most of the time I am painting though, or thinking about painting, or reading about painting.'

'But when you're not. I mean there seems so little to do.'

Simon rustled the tussock, drawing it through his hand. 'When I'm not painting what does it matter where I am,' he said quietly. Paul was embarrassed, as men are when passion is revealed. He stood up and looked out towards the plain.

'You can see for miles and miles,' he said.

'So you can,' said Vicky.

'In the summer you can hardly see the plain for the heat haze,' said Simon. Although they were talking to Paul, they were looking at each other. Paul had a sudden apprehension that they felt sorry for him.

'I reckon you would need to have a fair imagination to paint this country,' he said.

'In a way painting's all imagination,' said his brother.

They talked no more of it: not because it was too theoretical, but because it was too personal. The inner landscape of belief is hazardous ground. Together the three turned back, and began moving down the ridge. The wind came, breaking on them like a wave, making them gasp with the shock of it. The wind whistled around their ears, and they had to turn their heads to hear one another. 'By Jesus,' said Paul.

'Sometimes it comes suddenly,' said Simon. The tussock tops were laid back in the wind. There were occasional schist outcrops; and in their lee the sheep kept the earth bare by gathering. Yet there were no sheep as they went down that day. Paul took Vicky's arm and they angled across the wind, tacking to avoid its full force. Simon kept his head up, and his hair was swept back by the wind. 'It'll blow itself out by morning,' he shouted to them. There was something about the wind that was remarkable; something apart from the force, fierce cold, and abrupt arrival. That other thing was its purity. Nowhere on the hills did any refuse blow; no grit, no dust. The wind was harsh and clean, and blew over land that was just the same. The tussock shed nothing to the wind, and the wind was nothing but its own force.

Even in the bach Simon listened for the wind. Paul and Vicky kept by the kerosene heater, but Simon stood by the large studio window and watched the hills in the wind. Vicky turned his canvases, and Paul asked him why he hadn't gone to the High School reunion, and about visiting their parents. 'I've been meaning to go and see them again. I know I should, and I'm not a good writer,' Simon said. 'I just don't seem to have the time.' Paul was going to laugh, but then he had a sense almost of fear. He realized that his brother was serious; that he spent his time painting as a kind of compulsion. That he accepted it as an occupation and as a reasonable justification for not doing other things such as attending school reunions, or visiting parents. Paul felt for the first time that his condescension in regard to Simon's work might be equalled by Simon's contempt for his own.

'We've put in a new moulding machine from West Germany,' he said. 'We think by the end of the decade we'll have a twenty percent penetration of the Australian hard plastics market.' Paul watched his brother open his mouth to reply and find nothing honest to say. He only smiled. 'I had to pay twenty-five thousand dollars in tax last year,' Paul said, and gave a descending whistle. Then he wished that he'd said nothing. He wouldn't look at his wife.

'Hell, I didn't make ten thousand,' said Simon.

'I didn't make anything,' said Vicky.

'You've got more brains than any of us,' said Simon, 'and a better education.'

'That's true. That's quite true. I always tell her that myself.' Paul was eager to detract from himself. 'Even in business matters she always realizes what the essentials are. Vicky seems so good in reading people.' Vicky was interested in the canvases again; Simon had both hands in his pockets, and was looking away from his brother.

Paul began to examine the paintings, and as he made comments, Simon watched each of his paintings with the look between secret lovers whose glances meet while their elders talk of everyday things. 'None of them has any shadows,' said Vicky after a time.

'That's right,' said Paul. He'd felt something odd about them.

'An artist's vision is omniscient,' said Simon. It was a pretension to free him from the need to make any explanation, but Paul accepted it.

'So the artist is in fact superior in view to the sun, and through him the whole landscape is accessible.'

'Perhaps that,' said Simon, and he looked at Vicky as she smiled a little. He had no desire to mock his brother. Paul was pleased with the reason. He liked a logical explanation. With greater sympathy he looked again at the painting: perhaps there were other clues to the riddle of it.

In the evening they were closer. The three of them sat in the studio by the heater, and drank red wine. Paul and Simon were able to minimise their separation by talking of their boyhood, and recollecting the curious incidents that all boyhoods have. It became dark early, but they were happy with the light of the kerosene heater. The flame like a campfire displayed only the surfaces square to it. A cheek, a forehead, the side of a shoe, were seen clearly in the glow. The light was a kind blush that made Vicky's beauty more obvious. 'I envy you your wife,' said Simon. He gave a laugh that was more a shout. 'If only I had Vicky.' With the fierce admiration of an artist he saw the turn of her hair below the cheek, and the solidity of her breasts beneath the jersey. 'Women's flesh has such a weight,' he said in wonder. 'Why is it that women's flesh is so heavy. That's why it paints so well I guess.' Paul looked at his wife, and was excited by her beauty.

'You are beautiful; beautiful,' he said. It was a statement of observation, not possession. In his pleasure and admiration he was aware of sadness too, and didn't know why. He was close to tears.

'Both of you have drunk too much,' said Vicky.

'I have to go into town and visit a very skinny girl who works in dry-cleaning,' said Simon. Paul laughed; not at the skinny girl, but in exultation at the beauty of his wife. 'A dear, kind, skinny girl,' said Simon. 'She's the only one who'll have me. Everyone there thinks I'm a complete nutter. I did have a girl with heavier flesh; she used to come and live with me sometimes, but she married a land agent. They have a house of 1000 square metres.'

'How cruel you are about women,' said Vicky, though she was laughing too.

'The skinny girl has a better colour sense,' said Simon, 'but it's not an adequate compensation.' The glow of the heater held the line of their faces as they laughed.

Paul and Vicky talked about his brother, later in bed. As couples talk of the people they have been with, so that they can reach an accepted marital view of those around them. 'He's always had that spontaneity,' said Paul. 'Ever since a kid he's had this fresh view of things.'

'But then he's had no one to please but himself. Every time in his life a decision has had to be made, he's been able to follow his own priorities.'

'That's true.' They were lying close together on one of the single bed sides. Paul stroked his wife's breasts softly. He made friendly circles around the nipple with his finger. 'I sometimes feel that people without money like to despise it. Don't you think? Money isn't easy to make, but people like to think it is.' The wind was gusting about the bach. It made noises like someone striking the walls with a flat board.

'Simon doesn't think about money,' said Vicky. 'You can see that. He wants things the rest of us don't know how to talk about.' Certainly Paul didn't, but he lay there and knew that his wife was right. 'He wants to cut the world up and see inside perhaps,' she said.

'I think it's dangerous in a way,' said Paul. 'Making painting be everything, a religion and everything. For if you're wrong about it, if you've got nothing else …' It wasn't quite what he meant to say, and he lay thinking about it some more, and listening to the wind.

'If you don't hedge your bets you mean,' said Vicky.

They'd gone as far as they could. They lay and listened to the assault of the wind. 'There's no heating at all in this room you know,' said Paul. 'The kerosene heater in the studio is the only one he's got. He should have the heating laid on to the rock gas. In the morning it's going to be cold here.'

It was cold in the morning. Paul woke because of it, and his nose was like putty. His wife was curled towards him, and her forehead beneath the sheets pressed into his chest. She lay on her side and curled because of the cold. In the corners of the windows the frost had made patterns; hachured patterns like fossils in rock, and some like thick spider webs. He pushed himself carefully away from Vicky, keeping the blankets around her; not letting the cold air in. Even so, she murmured at his going. He found his slippers and dressing gown, and held the sides of the dressing gown together at his throat with one hand, as he went quietly to the kitchen.

Simon was painting. Standing in the winter dawn, with the light of the kerosene heater glowing behind him, he was at his work. He wore a thick jersey over his pyjamas, and two pairs of socks. Still drained by sleep, Paul stood in the kitchen and watched him through two doorways. Simon had an expression of complete absorption, more often seen in the faces of children than adults. If he turned away from the canvas, he did so in a haste to be facing it again, and when he used the brush he seemed to use it like a scalpel, cutting precisely into the canvas. At each cut his mouth moved, as if he were shaping words like there, and there, and there, to accompany each action. If the cut was a success he would work more urgently: there, and there, and there, with louder breathing that Paul could hear. If dissatisfied he might cough and glance away, wriggle his toes in their double thickness, before he was driven to the brush again. Simon's face in concentration was a picture itself of inward intensity; of hope and urgency impelled by vision. As Paul watched, he could feel the bland biology of his own face, with its heavy cheeks and cold morning nose. He moved to the bench and filled the jug. He used one of the rock gas rings which never gave any trouble, and stood shivering as he waited for the jug to heat. The lower part of the window glass was beaded with condensation, and he joined the drops with his finger as he stood there. Jesus, how Simon loves to paint, he thought. Painting his life away here, and nobody cares. Paul called to his wife that he was bringing coffee up, and when he went past, Simon was still working in the studio. Painting, painting; there, there, there, with the inspiration of a Christ.

'He's painting already,' Paul told Vicky.

'Well, he's got a heater in there, hasn't he.'

'He's at it like a masterpiece.'

'Maybe it is,' said Vicky. She stroked his wrist. 'How would we know.'

'How can he be sure then. Every artist can't be right.' They thought about that. The more they thought the more doubtful it seemed as a statement.

'Oh well,' said Vicky.

Simon was making breakfast for himself when Paul went through again. They talked, then Paul went into the studio by the heater. He looked at the painting. As always with his brother's work he could find no link between the man and the work; or even between the exhilaration of execution, and the result. The hills were triangles, and the sun livid, and scarred with the thick texture of the colours. The whole thing seemed to have a loss of symmetry which gave an uneasy tension. It looked only fifteen minutes work. Paul took the brush and charged it with yellow from the tray. He made a jab at the canvas; one more smear amongst many. It was an action of appeal, not malice. 'There's no snow today,' said Simon from the kitchen. 'Why not stay another day?' There was a letter on the tray that Simon must have been re-reading. The sharp creases where it had been folded made it rock when Paul touched the tray. He read the last lines.

'I can only take one more for the gallery, but believe me I think you're on the right way. Go on, go on. Remember Klee and Dubuffet.'

'Who's Klee?' said Paul, when he went back to Vicky.

'A symbolist I think. His reputation is on the crest of the wave.'

'I had a look at that painting he's doing. It's just like the rest. All layered savagery and colours that don't match.'

'For you everything must be a representation.'

'And this place smells. Do you suppose he ever cleans up around here. Four rooms, and each of them a mess. Below the window in the studio there's a whole line of dead insects.'

'Yes.'

'They crunch under your feet.'

'Squalor is an artist's privilege.' She was enjoying his indignation.

'It's a pity he can't get the land agent's wife out again.'

'She wasn't married then.'

'Whatever.'

Vicky began to dress, and as Paul watched her, he felt the best he had all morning. She made it an unconscious spectacle of graceful movements and feminine angles: bowing so that her hair swung, lifting her arms to draw her jersey on.

'Remember Klee and Dubuffet,' he said.

'Why do you say that?'

'Oh, nothing,' he said.

'Hmmm?'

'Just nothing.'

They left in the middle of the morning, when it began to snow. Simon said that if they were going to leave that day then it was better to go before it had been snowing for too long. Simon would have been content for them to stay; he was content for them to leave. Paul decided that his brother was impartial about all things, but one. Simon and Paul stood by the car for a time, and Vicky sat in the car, with the motor running and the heater on. 'We want you to come and stay with us soon,' said Paul.

'I really must do it,' said Simon. He looked past his brother, at the gathering snow in the air. 'The hills have gone,' he said. 'See how the snow has shrouded the hills.' There was no wind left, or they couldn't feel it, yet the snow came drifting in from the south, moving past them and rarely seeming to reach the ground. 'You said there'd be no snow today,' said Paul. He put out his hand to his brother.

'It's good to be wrong about snow.' Simon farewelled his brother, and put a kiss on to his hand then on to the window close to Vicky. He waved as they went down the track. He watched for a time the snow coming from the south. How it obscured the hills, and how it had to drop into the tussock for so long before any of it could be seen there. Then he went inside to paint.

It was quiet, driving in the snow. The expensive car was quiet and warm, and only the gravel crackled under the wheels; especially on the sharp corners around the spurs where the gravel had gathered in little drifts on the downhill side, mimicking snow. Paul and Vicky sat with their own thoughts, then he said, 'I saw him painting this morning. I watched him from the kitchen. He painted as if there were a naked woman before him instead of lines and colours. He painted as if there were nothing else in the world. Just him and the canvas. Do you know what I mean?' His wife smiled. 'I saw part of a letter from a gallery. It said that he should keep on with his own way of painting. Remember Klee and Dubuffet it said.'

'Both of them had a vision.' She seemed farther from him than she had for a long time.

'What chance can he possibly have. I mean here in the middle of Central Otago, and the whole damn country that isolated from the world's art anyway.' He laughed to emphasize to her how hopeless it was. Vicky leant back, and turned to watch the snow, seeming so ethereal at a distance, yet moving fast, and stinging on the glass by her face. 'He's forty-two now. He doesn't even own the place he lives in. He hides there, painting, painting, painting, as if his heart will break.' There was silence. Where the hills were closest the snow cloud was grey, but looking out of the hills and above them, the snow cloud was pearl, and the flakes slid out of it in a tracery.

'I left him a cheque,' said Paul. 'Just a couple of hundred.' He said it roughly, to minimise any sentiment.

'You may be rewarded yet,' said Vicky.

Paul thought he knew her mood. 'You think he can make it, don't you? You think he's going to be hailed a genius yet, and eclipse us all.' Paul was eager. 'That's it isn't it?' Vicky moved her head in impatience.

'But it doesn't make any difference,' she said. 'Can't you see. You've seen him painting. You said so yourself. Whatever it is that really matters he's got already, hasn't he?' She turned to him. Her eyes had affection, but he saw irony there as well. Pity for them both, and her hand rested on his arm, to help him bear her pity perhaps. Paul saw his brother again at his painting; the intense, closed face of his brother as he leant towards the canvas, and there, there, there, cutting with the brush. What did he care for anything else. There, there, there it was, all that meant anything.

Paul began to think of himself in a new way. As a successful man with a hairy stomach. A man who talked a lot about his possessions and import export regulations, watched television quiz shows, and was popular at Rotary. A man who kept his teeth clean in case some-one should want to look at them, and his current affairs up to date lest the conversation should turn that way. A man at ease in his environment. A man who moved happily from one thing to another in life, as a monkey moves briskly from one branch to the next. He determined to think carefully, and he drove carefully, the car drop-ping lower through the hills. 'Would you like to come to Sydney with me?' he asked his wife. 'Or we could go skiing perhaps when I come back. That rock gas setup in the bach works well enough doesn't it.' He wondered how many more years he would live, and if those years would be any different. 'All this country is so much the same,' he said in sudden exasperation at the anonymity of the snow and the road. Vicky stopped looking at the country which he thought so much the same. She moved her arm and stroked the back of his head, and then rested her hand on his shoulder.

'I don't think we should ever blame ourselves,' she said.

The snow was beginning to build. The first half-hour's snow had melted as it fell, but in doing so it took the last warmth from the ground, and the snow which fell later was crisp and gathered rapidly to mark those slight leading edges in the tussock that went unno-ticed at other times. The snow softened the outline of the ground they could see, and lay thickest along the bank side of the road. 'We must be nearly down to the plain again,' he said.

Demolition at Waipiata
1986
Egg Tempera on Gesso
670 x 1200mm
Private Collection

Glenavy
1989
Watercolour
570 x 760mm
Collection: Forrester Gallery, Oamaru

Sutton
1990
Egg Tempera on Gesso
505 x 720mm
Private Collection

Kokonga
1990
Watercolour
530 x 740mm
Private Collection

FLIGHT

On the slow wing-beat
of a curious falcon
my wishes belonged.
I rose and spiralled
in thermals
and the mountains smiled
all afternoon.

The falcon's wings
splintered the autumn sunlight
above the remnant fog
that sat on the river
like a marquee
and water scrawled inscriptions
on every stone.

Ben Ohau
1991
Oil on Canvas
1220 x 1220mm
Private Collection

UNDER THE HAWKDUNS

(for W. S. Merwin)

In the evening   first a rainbow
straddling the brown hills
that bounded the world of my youth

then late   towards the end of dusk
a gusty wind began to blow
shaking the tussock

and bronze clouds rose
behind the startled face
of the moon paravaning

like a high load poised
over the wheel of a cart

Timeless Land
1992
Oil on Canvas
760 x 1520mm
Private Collection

MADNESS AND THE MOUNTAIN

1

The morning heralds no new life for the mountain,
no new mountain. The snowgrass grows
or it doesn't: from its true source
the river flows down from the snows.

This morning the mountain wears
a fashionable poncho of mist.
Do not laugh at the mountain.
Rock and snow spells mountain for the eyes
yet the picture, unlike the tourist's instamatic view,
may differ in the mind,
spring dreams of a different, dangerous kind.

If we see the mountain as it can be,
as ally, then it's beautiful,
and we may safely label it a favourite,
though this unbiased, unrelenting
country has none.

Now we have a favourite mountain.

2

If I give praise
it is because I walk unmolested
among jumbled, broken rock
on a morning made to be used
but not undone.

I am learning to live with the mountain.

3

If the mountain should fall
then what hope is there for us?
And what hope for the ego-tripper
who dares the mountain
to take his life away
as quick as any quiet natural accident
could ever do?

Do not taunt the mountain.

4

The mountain is an obsession.

Good morning. And Brother Sun
good morning to you, too.

My feet move in time to the rhythm
of the bright morning
and the steady wind sweeping down from the saddle
carries no hint of passion, nor anger, nor sorrow.
To meet it head-on in the valley
and feel no guilt-inspired need to turn aside
is to release an ideal long shackled.

5

Gone the private thunder, absent
the rave of flood water
and the rattle of falling stones.

Something is at peace this morning
on the way to the mountain.

6

If I were to say
I am fortunate to feel the spangling sunlight
warm on my arms and face,
to see its glint on the river
that turns like a band of steel...

And if I were to say, too,
that the granite walls are wrinkled
like the hides of elephants,

then who is to say I am wrong?
and who would deny me the right to say it?
to say, That is how it is, is
how I like it to be...

Man, you are some mountain.

7

You cannot exorcise a memory.

Good morning, Mr Mountain, Sir.

To follow one's will up the mountain
is to leave a certain bullying life behind.

Come down from the mountain. What
will come down from the mountain?

Our time is but a short time in the life of a mountain.

Something is at peace this morning
that belongs, in part, to the mountain.

Something is at peace up there,
way up there on the mountain.

Canterbury Plains
1992
Oil on Canvas
760 x 1010mm
Private Collection

Ski Ohau
1992
Watercolour
560 x 760mm
Private Collection, Queenstown

DESCENT FROM THE FLUGELHORN

It was the third in a series of summer droughts. North Otago must be as bad for droughts as anywhere in the country, I guess. In March the landscape lay stretched and broken like the dried skin of a dead rabbit, shrunken away from the bones and sockets. The pale yellow clay showed through the tops of the downs like hip bones, and even the willows along the bed of the Waipohu stream had the blue-grey of attrition.

Wayne Stenning and I were selling raffle tickets so that the club could have new jerseys for the season. All over the district we went, and despite the cost of the petrol it was worth it. Most we called on had some connection with the club, and even if they didn't directly, then as country people they identified with the district name and gave anyway. Usually they bought whole books, not single tickets, which made the tripping about worthwhile. Wayne and I had been at it most of the afternoon, and we were cutting over the old quarry road to call at a last few houses. The dust was bad. Some people had oiled the road outside their gates, but it didn't seem to do much good. In any case you couldn't see where the dust had settled, for everything was much the same colour.

Wayne was pleasant company, always ready with a joke, or a laugh at somebody else's. He'd been training most of the summer. Keen as mustard he was, and with some cause. Last season he made the local representative side and got his name in the rugby almanac's list of players worth watching from lesser unions. He had the right build for a prop — not all that tall, but his chest was so thick that his clothes hung out all round and made him look fat, which he wasn't.

I hadn't realized that Bernie Dalgety lived on that road, but we turned into a farm and found him at the yards, sorting a few sheep. I'd met him a few times at the gun club. He took three books. The only drawback was that Wayne got some grease on his slacks when we sat on the drill, waiting for Bernie to get the money. Wayne said

they were his best trousers and his wife would be peeved; he hadn't been married long. He couldn't stay worried, however, and told Bernie the joke about the librarian and the lion tamer. He did a bit of running on the spot, too, before we got back into the car — said he'd been having some trouble with cramp in the thigh muscles. Bernie and I told him the cause of that and he laughed, but said he was serious. I hadn't begun any training myself. I'd reached the stage at which the most usual adjective applied to my game was 'experienced'. Anyone who sticks with the game reaches that point eventually — a sort of watershed after which you're no longer capable of improving, and it takes cunning to disguise the fact that you've gone back.

We nearly missed the place after Dalgety's. It was in a fold of the downs, and well back from the road. New farmhouses go for a view; prominence before all else. The old houses of the district seem to have been sited chiefly with the idea of escaping the wind. There was no cattlestop, and no name on the letter-box. Wayne opened the gate and told me he'd close it and run up after me. Needed the exercise, he said, so I went on. The drive wasn't used much, I could tell, for the dry grass in the centre strip scratched and flurried underneath the car as I drove. I could see Wayne in the rear-vision mirror, jogging easily along, doing a few quick knees-up from time to time. He let his arms hang loosely and flapped his hands to ensure relaxation. Our coach was very keen on relaxation; he trained anyone who would turn up three hours a night in the name of relaxation.

The house was of old-fashioned dark brick. It had window-bays that bulged outwards and heavy, green tiles. The shrubs and trees must once have been in ordered harmony with the house, but in old age had attained a freakish disproportion. Shattered pines along the south side reached over the tiles and mounds of their needles lay in the guttering. The path to the front door was obstructed by the growth of a giant rhododendron, mostly wood, but with a few clusters of leaves that defied the drought. The tall macrocarpa hedge down the other side had been cut so often that there was little foliage, rather a series of massive, convoluted branches that seemed barely contained in the rectangular shape the years had imposed on them.

Wayne and I avoided the rhododendron and walked along the concrete path towards the back door. At the far corner of the house was a sun-porch that had been glassed in comparatively recently, for its large panes contrasted with the windows of the rest of the house. Wayne stopped suddenly at the corner, and I stumbled into him from behind. 'There's someone in there,' he said. 'We can ask him.' We stood a little foolishly by the glass doors and looked in. The place was well chosen, for despite the hedge the late afternoon sun was a warm pressure on the backs of our heads, and suffused the room with an amber glow. The rich and heavy light was liquid, and its slow currents bore dust that glinted and eddied, dissipating the shape of the dark dresser and falling like a fragile veil in front of the old man who sat facing us.

The old man was dressed, but over his clothes he wore a pink candlewick chenille dressing-gown, and in front of the cane chair he sat in, his zipped leather slippers stuck out, shiny and without the wrinkles of wear. Something in their positioning made it seem they had been placed by another, rather than the random result of move-ment. A green towel lay across his lap, and his hands rested there, the fingers curled and trembling slightly. 'Hullo,' said Wayne. He said it uncertainly, because he felt odd speaking through the closed door, yet he couldn't keep looking in at the old man only a few feet away without saying something. There was no coarseness of age in the old man's face; no warts, enlarged pores, or tufts of hair. He seemed to have passed the time of excrescences, and like driftwood only the essential shape and grain remained. His head and face were entirely smooth, polished even; the skin in the amber of the afternoon sun

responding with a slight sheen.

'Don't think the old coot heard me,' said Wayne softly, and he turned his face away to snigger uneasily. The old man's neck did not stand up from his collar, or the folds of the candlewick dressing-gown, instead it protruded parallel with the ground like the neck of a tortoise, and so his head, to keep his abstracted gaze level, was tilted back. His head and neck were not directly forward, however, but rested more along the line of his left shoulder.

When I was a boy I had a favourite marble with a coloured spiral at the centre of the glass. Gradually the surface got crazed; little pits and star bruises appeared on the glass until it was almost opaque and the coloured spiral had lost its vividness. The old man's eyes were like that, and the lower lids had fallen away somewhat, revealing moist, red linings that emphasised the bruised, opaque eyes, and con-trasted with the pale sheen of his skin.

Wayne would have opened the door, but the old man was alone in the room, and there didn't seem much point. We carried on round the house until the back door, and we knocked and waited there. After seeing the old man Wayne needed reassurance of his youth. He performed several jumps from the crouch, leaping towards the tiled roof and patting the guttering. No one came to the door in answer to our knocks, or Wayne's acrobatics. 'Strange sort of an out-fit,' he said. 'There must be someone else about, surely.' We were going to leave when there was a lot of noise from hens, and moving round the edge of the hedge we saw a woman feeding white leghorns on the bare ground in front of the farm sheds.

She was a big woman, in cardigan and dark stockings despite the heat. She came heavily towards us, the last hens falling off behind her when they realised she had no more grain. In one hand was an old milking bucket half-filled with eggs, and she leant to the other side against the weight. At a distance she didn't look so old, but when she was close, though the strength was still there, the age was more apparent; rosettes of pigment stained her skin, and as she set the bucket down before us the swollen joints of her fingers clasped on the handle had difficulty releasing, nearly pulling the bucket over.

'We're selling raffle tickets on behalf of the Waipohu rugby club. For new jerseys.' Wayne seemed to assume that all old people were deaf, and he shouted into her face.

'Where have you been?' she said in reply. Wayne didn't know how to answer that, but she meant what other people in the district had we visited, and as we told her the ones we could remember, she murmured 'Yes, yes', as if the familiar names established our authenticity. Her voice was flat and worn, but steady enough. She came back with us to the house, refusing to have the bucket carried for her. 'Dad would like to see you,' she said. 'I'll take a ticket for Dad.' Dad must have been her husband, not her father, yet the term she adopted for convenience in family times had stuck. Culland was the name she wanted on the ticket. I wrote it for her, because she said she found writing difficult; watching her swollen fingers attempting to get money from her purse, we could understand. That was later, though. First she left the eggs at the back door, and took us through the dark, wainscoted hall to the sunroom to see Dad.

The old man hadn't shifted, but we approached him from a different angle, and like a figurine his aspect altered. He'd been a big man once, but his shoulders seemed folded, and the pink, candlewick chenille fell away loosely. 'These young people are from the Waipohu rugby club, Dad,' said Mrs Culland as we sat along the window seat, the sun behind us again, the golden dust drifting once more before the old man's face. 'Selling raffle tickets, Dad,' she said. Wayne nodded his head and chuckled, as if selling raffle tickets was a good joke he wanted the old man to share. Mrs Culland said nothing for some time; she forgot us and had a rest, breathing slowly and massaging the joints of each finger in turn.

'Well,' said Wayne brightly, in a manner that preceded comments about really being on our way and so on. Neither responded. Mrs Culland continued to rest, and the old man's terrapin neck and head remained extended, his eyes unblinking, and his hands trembling on the green towel. The mainspring of the world seemed to have run down, and time was held back in the amber warmth of the sunroom. The macrocarpa shadows stole further across the dry lawn, and the sound of Mrs Culland's coarse, swollen hands as she rubbed them together was like the sighing of a distant sea. Even Wayne stopped fidgeting and sat resigned, reading again the prizes listed on the raffle books he held. Three days at Mount Cook in the off-season, or the cash equivalent, was first prize.

'Dad played rugby,' said Mrs Culland. 'Not here though — in Southland. All his family played.'

'Great game,' said Wayne a little patronisingly, and flexed the heavy muscles of his outstretched leg.

'Played for the South Island twice,' she said in her flat voice. 'Booby Culland everyone called him then.' She pronounced it as a title, and heaving herself up went to the dresser and returned with a photo of her husband in the South Island team.

'South Island,' said Wayne in an altered voice. The transience of it all seemed to catch him. Booby Culland's photo showed the arrogance of youth and strength. Guiltily, Wayne looked from the photo to the old man and quickly away again. 'Lock,' he said.

'That's right,' said Mrs Culland.

'Line-out specialist, I suppose.'

'Yes.'

Mrs Culland leant forward from the window seat, and held the old man's nearer arm, so that for a moment the hand stopped trembling. 'We're talking about football, Dad,' she said. 'Football.' The old man opened his mouth slightly, but if he wanted to speak he was prevented by his top dentures, which slipped down exposing a swollen seam of artificial gum, as if he were bringing something up. Mrs Culland released his arm matter-of-factly and pushed his chin up. But briefly his opaque, bruised eyes focused in revelation; for an instant the prisoner could be seen from the shadows and behind the bars. 'Football, Dad,' she said again.

He tried once more. 'Descent from the Flugelhorn.' His voice was almost identical to that of his wife — worn and even, as if she had adopted the practice of ventriloquism.

'No, Dad, football. You know.'

'Descent from the Flugelhorn,' he repeated, and his eyes turned away. A thin skein of spittle ran from his mouth down the pink chenille of his left shoulder, touching it with amber spangles in the sunlight. Mrs Culland pushed his chin up again. 'He was very keen on music,' she said, in a form of explanation. 'As he got older and the boys took over the property, he turned to music.' There was another pause, and we sat subdued in the unrepentant sun of the summer drought.

'Lived for his football, though, as a young man. No doubt about that. They all did in his family, but Booby Culland was the best of them. Played in the provincial side fifty-one times, and was made captain for Southland on the day of his last game.' Wayne took it as a blow more than anything else. He still held the photo, and he cast about for other things to rest his gaze upon apart from the old man. 'I'll show you the jersey,' said Mrs Culland. I tried to tell her it wasn't necessary, but she had become accustomed to following her own will, and went off into the rest of the house.

'Jesus, it's hot in here,' said Wayne. 'We'd better push off soon. There are other places yet, and we don't want to be too late.'

As we waited the old man gave three sharp inward breaths, and then, as if something had given way at the centre of him, his shoulders folded still further. His big, translucent hands gripped the green towel in his lap, and one foot extended on the wooden floor of the porch so that the soft sole of the leather slipper squeaked as it moved. There seemed to be no breathing out. 'Jesus,' said Wayne. The old man looked much the same, but his posture gradually slackened, and although his neck still lay along his shoulder, his face turned down and lost its level gaze. 'Jesus,' said Wayne, and stood with his hands into fists as I tried to feel the old man's pulse.

Mrs Culland thought he'd just had a turn when she came back, but when she realised he was dead, she let the jersey slide into his lap with the towel, and began to stroke the smooth grain of his head. She didn't weep, she didn't even sit down; she stood beside him and it seemed as if her flesh had settled more heavily as her cupped hands moved clumsily over his head. We asked if we could help, but she said she could get in touch with everyone by phone. 'I did pay you, didn't I?' she said, and when she was satisfied of that she let us go. We never thought to use the sunroom door — perhaps it didn't open, anyway. We went out the back door, and as we passed the windows on our way to the car neither of us looked in.

Wayne called jerkily to me that he would run on a little, and I didn't hurry after him. If he wanted the chance to run it out then I didn't mind. Sooner or later he'd find it didn't work with everything. I let the car idle down the drive, the grass rustling beneath the chassis. Wayne had gone a fair way. As I shut the gate I could see him up the road, running hard along the grass verge. He ran a mile or so, and when I found him he had reached the dip and was sitting below a willow in the dry streambed. As I got out of the car I could hear him crying, and I went over and sat with him, the fine willow roots draped like hessian down the bank behind us.

The light began to change, but the evening was still hot, with no promise of rain. Homecoming magpies began their harsh calls in the trees around us, and a Landrover came through, travelling towards Cullands', rolling out dust clouds that we could barely see, but which had their own flinty taste. Wayne had stopped crying, and dug with a twig in the sand and leaves. 'Sorry about that,' he said. He gave a rather shy smile. 'Do you think everyone gets the feeling some time or other that they've passed themselves going the other way?'

'Yes.'

It was all we had to say about it, and it was enough. It doesn't always help to tease things out, to dissect our experiences like schooldays' frogs. As we stood up to go the magpies began a great racket, and some flew off in protest, the wing beats whistling in the still air. 'I've ruined these tweeds of mine,' said Wayne. As well as the oil stain he'd torn them along the upper seams, where the sweat had made them grip as he ran.

'Put them down to experience,' I said as we went back to the car, and he smiled again at that. He hoped his wife would understand, he said.

Southern Crossing
1992
Oil on Canvas
920 x 1370mm
Collection: Artist

EPIPHANIES

may not be the stuff
of reality, but

they are
amply

fulfilling. You could
say they're

on the way
to the paradise

that keeps its
distance

and grins
like the thin

hinge of yellow
light

pressed on the
skyline's rim

before it's
nearly dark,

or perhaps
it's not

like anything
we can imagine –

epiphanous.

Away to the South
1993
Oil on Canvas
915 x 1370mm
Private Collection, Dunedin

Winter 1992: Mount St Bathans
1993
Oil on Canvas
660 x 1220mm
Collection: Anna Lise Seifert, Dunedin

Memorial Hall
1993
Oil on Canvas
760 x 1520mm
Private Collection, Rangiora

THE STOPOVER

When the trout rise like compassion
it is worth watching

when the hinds come down
from the hills
with a new message

it will be as well to listen

GRASS

I am this country's
most gratifying herbage

animals uplift
and chew me

I pass through
smooth wet chutes

lodge in warm red
bowels

before my seed
is ejected

snuggles in to the soil
and beds down again

in the earth
I outlive those

who indiscriminately
use and expel me

and whose bones
fall into my frail arms

and crumble
while only

the sky
looks on

Gidding Downs
1993
Oil on Canvas
840 x 1520mm
Private Collection

132

THERE IS A PLACE ...

There's a place, not far, sweet country if only it had summer rain. The sheep seek shade, and in these camps the loess clay of the ground is smooth and hard, or pooled to dust, and the droppings of the sheep are thickly spread, but dry and inoffensive, baked in the heat. In the odd sink hole the briar seeks moisture and gorse blooms brighter than the clay. The ridges are worn almost bald, like the heads of the lean, brown farmers who ride farm bikes too small for them across the paddocks of their land. The creek beds are marked more by rushes and willows than running water, and the mallards come only in twos or threes. An easterly is always up after midday and burnishes the arc of pale, blue sky. The shelter belts close to the road and the macrocarpa before the farmhouse, are dusted with a false pollen drifting in off the road. The rural delivery boxes are large so that stores can be left there as well as mail, and each has a name painted by hand. In the evenings the sheep come to the stock dams and troughs to drink, the magpies gather to imitate the noise of poets, and the barley grass and brown-top ripple at the sides of the shingle roads.

Is that so far away?

CROSSING THE CANTERBURY PLAINS

The field shines with the light of cut corn
           and quite far off
    a solitary pine needles a solitary cloud
but I don't care
    for we seem to be safe here
where nothing vexes the sky
      that's clear to the mountains
and beyond.
          When the sun shines
even autumn's haughty out here
      where a leaf might be blown a hundred miles
    and end up somewhere much the same.
That's plains, they
    make you bound to live
within the bounds of where you are;
      no next valley to explore,
    no nearby hills to scale
      looking for a hint of promised land.
We may travel to the ends of the earth
    and back again
      and never know whether
the beetle hunched between stalks
    feels sorrow, or if the distant clouds
quivering with white light
    drift forever.

Taieri Pet Over Rocklands
1994
Oil on Canvas
455 x 560mm
Marshall Seifert Gallery

SPACES

In essence they are austere:
light shimmers there

across the downs and above,
but you cannot ever prove

that what was everywhere
once, was ever austere

as sky is when cloud is not
and we are all we've got

Maniototo Evening
1994
Oil on Canvas
835 x 1220mm
Private Collection

Ohau
1994
Oil on Canvas
1070 x 1070mm
Private Collection

REQUIEM IN A TOWN HOUSE

Mr Thorpe came off sixteen hundred hectares of hill country when he finally retired, and his wife found a Town House for them in Papanui. Town House is a euphemism for a free standing retirement flat, and retirement flat is a euphemism for things best left so disguised.

Mr Thorpe made no complaint to his wife when he first saw the place of his captivity. She had accepted a firmament of natural things for forty years, and he had promised her the choice of their retirement. Yet as the removal men brought those possessions which would fit into the new home, Mr Thorpe stood helplessly by, like an old, gaunt camel in a small enclosure. Merely by moving his head from side to side he could encompass the whole of his domain, and being long-sighted by nature and habit, he found it hard to hold the immediate prospect of their section in focus.

It wasn't that Mr Thorpe had come to the city determined to die. He didn't give up without a struggle. He was a farmer and a war veteran. He went to church on Sundays with his wife, and listened to the vicar explaining the envelope donation system. He joined the bowling club, and learned which side had the bias. But he could not escape a sense of loss and futility even amid the clink of the bowls, and he grew weary of being bullied by the swollen chested women at afternoon tea time.

Mrs Thorpe developed the habit of sending her husband out to wait for the post. It stopped him from blocking doorways, and filling up the small room of their Town House. He would stand at the letter box, resting his eyes by looking into the distance, and when the postman came he would start to speak. But the postman always said Hello and Goodbye before Mr Thorpe could get anything out. There might be a letter from their daughter in Levin, a coloured sheet of specials from the Sooper Doop Foodmarket, or something from the *Reader's Digest* which he had been especially selected to receive. It

wasn't the same thing as being able to have a decent talk with the postman though.

The Town House imposed indignities on Mr Thorpe: its mean conception was the antithesis of what he had known. To eat his meals he must sit at what appeared to be a formica ironing board with chrome supports. It was called a dining bar. After a meal Mr Thorpe would stand up and walk three paces to the window to see the traffic pass, and three paces back again. He would look at the knives in their wall holders, and wonder at his shrunken world. He had to bathe in a plastic water-hole beneath the shower. His arthritis prevented him from washing his feet while standing, and he had to crouch in the water-hole on his buttocks, with his knees like two more bald heads alongside his own. He thought of the full length metal and enamel bath on the farm. Sometimes he went even further back, to the broad pools of the Waipounae River in which he swam as a young man. The bunched cutty grass to avoid, the willows reaching over, the shingle beneath. The turn and cast of the water in the small rapids was like the movement of a woman's shoulder; and the smell of mint was there, crushed along the side channels as he walked.

In the Town House even the lavatory lacked anything more than visual privacy. It was next to the living room: in such a house everything in fact is next to the living room. Mrs Thorpe's Bridge friends could hear the paper parting on its perforation, and reluctantly number the deposits. Mrs Thorpe would talk more loudly to provide distraction, and her husband would sit within the resounding hardboard, and twist his face in humiliation at the wall.

The hand-basin was plastic, shaped like half a walnut shell, and too shallow to hold the water he needed. The windows had narrow aluminium frames which warped in his hand when he tried to open them. The front step was called a patio by the agent, and the wall beside it was sprayed with coloured pebbles and glue.

The section provided little comfort for Mr Thorpe. The fences separating his ground from his neighbours' were so vestigial that he found it difficult not to intrude. One evening as he stood in the sun, like a camel whose wounded expression is above all, he was abused by McAlister next door for being a nosey old fool. Mr Thorpe was enjoying the feel of the sun on his face, and thinking of his farm, when he became aware that he was facing the McAlisters as they sunbathed on a rug. Mrs McAlister had a big stomach, and legs trailing away from it like two pieces of string. 'Mutton headed old fool,' McAlister said, after swearing at Mr Thorpe over the fence. Mr Thorpe turned away in shame, for he was sensitive concerning privacy. 'Oih. Go away you nosey old fool,' shouted McAlister.

After that Mr Thorpe unconsciously exaggerated his stoop when he was in his section, to reduce the amount of his body which would appear above the fences, and he would keep his eyes down modestly as he mowed the apron lawn, or tipped his rubbish into the bag.

He tried walking in the street, but it was too busy. The diesel trucks doused him with black fumes, and most of the children used the footpath to ride bikes on. The pedestrian lights beckoned him with Cross Now, then changed to Don't Cross whenever he began.

Mr Thorpe took to sleeping in the garage. In the corner was a heavy couch that had been brought in from the farm, but wouldn't fit in the house. It was opposite the bench on which he'd heaped his tools and pots of dried up paint. At first he maintained a pretence of occupation between bouts of sleep, by sorting screws, nails, tap-washers, and hose fittings into margarine pottles. As his despair deepened he would go directly to the couch, and stretch out with his head on the old, embroidered cushion. It was one place in which he didn't have to stoop. He had an army blanket with a stripe, for he had begun to feel the chill which is of years, not weather. There he would

lie in the back of the garage, free from the traffic, the McAlisters, and the confines of his own Town House. He had always been able to sleep well, and in retirement he slept even better. He was granted the release of sleep.

Mr Thorpe would lie asleep with his mouth open, and his breath would whine and flutter because of the relaxed membranes of his mouth and throat. His face had weathered into a set configuration, but it was younger somehow when he slept. His wife played Bridge in the living room with her friends, or watched programmes of glossy intrigue. Mr Thorpe lay in the garage, and revisited all the places from which he has drawn his strength. Age is a conjuror, and it played the trick of turning upside down his memory, so that all he had first known was exact and fresh again, and all the things most recent were husks and faded obscurity. Mr Thorpe talked with his father again, soldiered again, courted again, yet when he was awake he forgot the name of the vicar with whom he shook hands every Sunday, and was perplexed when asked for the number of his own Town House. Waking up was the worst of all. Waking from the spaciousness and immediacy of past experience, to the walls of his small bedroom closing in, or the paint pots massing on the garage bench.

'He sleeps all the time, just about,' Mrs Thorpe told the doctor, and Mr Thorpe gave a smile which was part apology for being able to sleep so well. 'He must sleep for sixteen or seventeen hours of the twenty-four sometimes. He sleeps most of the day in the garage.'

'Ah, he's got a hideaway then,' said the doctor. He used a jocular tone, perhaps because he was afraid of the response to any serious enquiry. Let sleeping dogs lie is a sound enough philosophy. 'You need more sleep when you're older,' said the doctor. He'd forgotten that the last time Mrs Thorpe came on her own account, he'd told her that old people don't need as much sleep.

'And he hasn't got the same energy anymore. Not the energy he once had. His interest in things has gone. Hasn't it, Rob?' Mr Thorpe smiled again, and was about to say that he missed the farm life, when his wife and the doctor began to discuss the medication he should have.

He never did take any of the medicine, but after the visit to the doctor he tried briefly to interest himself in being awake, for his wife's sake. He sat in front of the television, but no matter how loud he had it, the words never seemed clear. There was a good deal of reverberation, and laughter from the set seemed to drown out the lines before he caught their meaning. He could never share the contestant's excitement in the origin of the term *deus ex machina*.

A dream began to recur. A dream about the Town House in Papanui. In the dream he could feel himself growing larger and larger, until he burst from the garage and could easily stand right over the house, and those of his neighbours. And he would take the Town House, all the pressed board, plastic and veneers, and crush it as easily as you crush the light, moulded tray when all the peaches have been eaten. Then in his dream he would start walking away from the city towards the farmland. He always liked that best in his dream. He was so tall that with each stride he could feel the slipstream of the air about his head, and the hills came up larger with every step, like a succession of held frames.

He told his wife about the dream. She thought it amusing. She told him that he never could get the farm out of his head could he. She said he should ask McAlister if he would like to go fishing.

In the dream Mr Thorpe never reached the hills; he never actually got to be where he was walking so forcefully to in the dream. But he seemed to be coming closer time by time. As he drew nearer, he thought it was the country that he knew. The hills looked like the upper Waipounae, and he thought that he would soon be able to hear the cry of the stilts, or the sound of the stones in the river during the thaw, or the flat, self-sufficient whistle made by the southerly across the bluffs at the top of the valley.

Sunset near Omarama
1994
Oil on Canvas
712 x 1117mm
Collection: Robin Judkins, Christchurch

Ida Valley
1995
Oil on Canvas
760 x 1060mm
Private Collection, Wellington

WALKING IN

The country throbs
and all that is dead
is buried by all that's
so convincingly alive.

We sweat. The dusty earth
believes we are crying
yet the river sings.
We hate the steep bits,

love the easy grades
down from the bluffs,
the way the body
handles it all

as long as we don't
over-reach ourselves.
Let's go on reaching.
We carry all we need,

we think we know
where we're heading
and why, and two words
dwarf all others: living, here.

NAMING THE LOST

Clouds pursue each other north
        but that is all they do
and I don't envy them
            such futile purpose.

Expect no messages, no
        instructions from the sky,
    just limitless space
            for the storage of dreams,

for the making of dreams.
        All afternoon I've watched
    frayed blue patches
            shuffled across the sky

and tried to ignore
        your whip of complaints.
    You wish that nothing you love
            should ever change, that

all secrets be divulged
        and none should bring us sorrow.
    Well, tell me this:
            whose tattered flag

is waving to us
        foolhardy as courage? Whose
    banner flaps like a goose's wing,
            who's going to tell you

what you'd rather not hear,
        and who's going to
    name what you didn't know
            you'd lost?

TANGATA WHENUA

The station's a yellowy white box
surrounded by tarry gravel
dry grass
and an emptiness that seems to go on
and on

and the railway line's
a silent arrow
buried in a cutting
now that trains
don't run

the huge sky
ekes out the summer twilight
and down by the river
two piebalds are stroked by shadows
from the willows

the country
rolls through me
and stretches away as I lie back
and wait for the first bright stars
to prick the quilted sky

ANCESTORS

(for Phil Temple)

I came this way to shed some care.
Every stone I stumbled on, every

root that snagged my foot was
bastard discontent. By the time

I'd reached the hut I was too tired
to complain anymore. Shucking my pack

I lay in the grass that shimmered
in the breeze. The blue sky

preened itself. Wheels of sunlight
bowled along the valley. I dozed off

until evening crept over forest
and mountain. I knew they would

find me sometime. My speechless ancestors
played like mice among my dreams.

It grew cold. And colder. I woke
to the river running over my bed

of stone. I have come to know
that where a river sings a river

always sang. I listen.
This much I have learned.

Twizel
1995
Watercolour
560 x 750mm
Private Collection, Auckland

THERE IS A PLACE ...

There are other places, aren't there? There's the old place in the North Otago downs, where the pink road of crushed Ngapara gravel is bordered by gorse hedges with clay sods to fill the gaps, and the road runs up the small valley like a stream, and the shoulders of the downs are ringed with sheep tracks. Useless pines around the farm buildings heap the pig-pen, drill shed and fowl run with brown needles, and on the shattered branches which weep a whitening resin, the cones are fully open in the drought. There are single cabbage trees on the hillsides, and rilled, limestone outcrops, grey where the weathered surface is undisturbed, yellow in the overhangs where the sheep pack in to find the shade. The yellow-ginger ground of the drought has only the thistles green. The house, see, has a red tin roof and a dish to suck a little glamour down from the satellites. Yet the letter box at the end of the track has a tin flag which can signal to the rural delivery in the same old way, the magpies squabble in the woolshed pines, and in the copper evening skies the gulls fly slowly back to the shore. But you know all that.

Stock Pond with Harrier
1995
Oil on Canvas
660 x 1220mm
Private Collection

NOTES BY THE CONTRIBUTORS

Grahame Sydney

I write this with gratitude to my mother, Betty, and my late father, Jack Sydney (1912 - 1986) whose influence never leaves me – for their unselfish love and unquestioning encouragement. I hope I can do as well.

My father, London-born and youngest in a large family, had determined early that his own family would always have two homes: the Dunedin one, and a holiday house if he was able. Karitane, on the Otago coast, was the second home for us and the setting for many of my happiest childhood memories until in my early teens the appeal of the inland became too strong, and the family purchased a property at Arrowtown. Brown, burning summer heat, raw extremes of winter cold, and vast, empty and silent landscapes replaced the green, softer coastal images of my earlier holidays.

Scarcely a school break would pass without us being in Central, and steadily the long drives westward through the solitude of valleys and over the rocky ranges seeped into me: the strangeness of the dry rainshadow regions on such a narrow island, the surrealistic forms of the monumental rock stacks, and always that sense of a land almost untouched, even primeval. The land so huge, the man so small, so insignificant on its surface. I have never lost that sense – that awe.

Through teenage summers I grappled with the difficulty of watercolours, or grubbed away at the banks of the Arrow River, panning for tiny glints of gold in the black sand. Thin luck. At this time also Harry Vye Miller (1907-1986), artist and teacher, began a significant interest in my work which continued long beyond Saturday morning classes, sitting at our wooden school desks in the red brick suburban studio.

After my years at Otago University and Secondary College in Christchurch I returned to Central to teach at Cromwell District High School (1971-72), working towards my first one-man exhibition, learning what I could of oil painting methods and developing the characteristics which would later find more mature form in many of the paintings in this book. That Moray Gallery exhibition, (Dunedin, December 1972) provided the first promise of a painting life, and when I left New Zealand for Europe in early 1973 it was with the secret hope that I might indeed become an artist – a real painter – over there.

It never happened. As the silhouette of New Zealand's hills faded in the distance and slipped below the horizon, so, largely, did my urge to paint. In the eighteen months away I did very little work: nothing moved me enough, I was homesick, lonely, and increasingly my London dreams were visited by startling

visions of Central Otago's clarity, the enormity of the sky, its intense blues, the pervading silence, and wide, low footings of parched landscape. Not London.

By mid-1974 I knew what I wanted to do: my parents cheerfully agreed to help for an initial year, and my head was filled with involuntary pictures. Within a few weeks I was living in a small cottage at Naseby, in the aching chill of a bitter Otago winter. A painter now, working at last on the first of my Maniototo images. Back.

Over twenty years later I've not strayed far. Sometimes it's the Mackenzie Basin which calls me, sometimes the low horizon of the Canterbury Plains; but always images of the less spectacular valleys and mountain blocks of Central Otago's core maintain their grip on my painter's instinct, and I have learned to trust it utterly. Mysterious to me, that instinct resists explanation, but guides my hand.

G.S. September 1995

Brian Turner

I've always sought places which excite me, in which I feel liberated and at home. Places where I can feel free to look and listen, be both stimulated and at ease. Solace, solitude, clear air, bright light; places where the spirit takes flight.

I grew up hearing people, so many of them with an eye cocked to overseas (panters and cringers they were to me, people given to patronising their own), say that New Zealand was small. By the time I was 15 or 16 I was convinced they were wrong. I'd discovered inland Otago, then the high country of the South Island generally. It didn't feel small, it felt huge (sky, mountains, rivers, valleys) and grand. It still does. It was *my* place, *our* place, a place that 'belonged' to all of us that chose to live here irrespective of our racial background. I never felt daunted or suppressed by it, rather the opposite. Here I was engaged by and drawn to my country as never before. Here was an environment which made human pettinesses and the lust for power seem piffling, contemptible. Here was an environment which helped dissolve and wither the worst of me, gave me a better sense of what's enduring.

I'd been visiting Central Otago, for example, for years, and had grown to love it long before I met Grahame Sydney or became aware of his work. But when I did, talked with him, and got to know his paintings, I soon found that his responses and feelings for this country were similar to mine. He painted his visions, his heartfelt responses; I wrote mine down. Though neither of us is religious in the usual sense of the term, I think we both acknowledge our feelings of awe for the grace and majesty of the country, are aware of a sense of the numinous embodied in it.

I have never sat down in front of one of Grahame Sydney's paintings and deliberately set out to write a poem 'about' it. But, now and then, when paintings of his have come to the forefront of my mind, I have found myself wanting to express some thoughts about them. Occasionally this has extended to observations on the nature of art itself. Hence the poems 'Towards the Maniototo' and 'Landscapes of Central Otago', for instance. All told I find a surprisingly large number of my poems – including many not included in this book – seem to *fit*, to *go* with Sydney's art. I hope readers will agree.

As for Owen Marshall, I know that he shares my liking for many of the places evoked in Sydney's work, and it's clear that many of the fictional characters of his stories do too.

Over time we three have become firm friends. It is my pleasure to be associated with them in the publication of this book.

B.T. September 1995

Owen Marshall

Most of my life has been spent in the South Island towns of Blenheim, Oamaru and Timaru, although I was born in Te Kuiti in 1941. I grew up part of a family in which the world of literature and that of physical experience were equally valued. My father, a Methodist minister, passed on to me a love of books and an enthusiasm for nature, particularly through walking and camping.

After graduating M.A. (Hons) in History from the University of Canterbury, I became a full-time secondary teacher, mainly at Craighead Diocesan School, Timaru, and Waitaki Boys' High School, Oamaru. In 1985 I resigned from Waitaki as Acting Rector in order to have more time for my fiction, and in the nineties most of my time has been given to writing, although I also tutor at Aoraki Polytechnic in Timaru.

Nine books of mine have been published, most recently a novel, *A Many Coated Man*, and a collection of short stories, *Coming Home in the Dark*. A radio play, *An Indirect Geography* commissioned by Radio NZ, was first broadcast in 1991.

I live in Timaru with my wife, Jackie, and we have two daughters, Andrea and Belinda. Jackie and I have links with farming families in New Zealand going back to the 1840s, and feel very much at home with the landscape around us. I feel no particular attraction towards city life, and the term regionalist is one that I'm happy to apply to myself. The downlands of South Canterbury and North Otago are very familiar, and I enjoy the sometimes bleak grandeur of the Mackenzie Country and Central Otago.

Among friendships important to me are those with my partners in this book, Brian Turner and Grahame Sydney, with whom I have a fellowship of attitude as well as a common South Island context. It was through Brian that I came to know Grahame, and for a good many years now I have had the privilege not only of seeing some of his paintings taking shape, but in being aware of the life and the intelligence from which they arise. There is a wonderful lack of deceit in his work, and a wonderful presence of landscape on its own terms.

Despite the visual and naturalistic elements sometimes remarked on in my writing, and emphasised perhaps within the selection chosen for this book, I'm more an impressionist than a strict realist, and the psychological landscapes of my fellow New Zealanders are my fundamental concern. My interest is in mood and character more than plot and action, and a search to capture the fragrance of experience, rather than experience itself. What I look for in all arts, is some insight into the business of living.

O.M. September 1995